DODGER!

Jim Eldridge

MSCHOLASTIC

For Lynne, my constant inspiration

Scholastic Children's Books
Euston House, 24 Eversholt Street,
London, NW1 1DB, UK

A division of Scholastic Ltd
London ~ New York ~ Toronto ~ Sydney ~ Auckland
Mexico City ~ New Delhi ~ Hong Kong

Published in the UK by Scholastic Ltd, 2011

Text copyright © Jim Eldridge, 2011
Cover image copyright © Richard Jones, 2011

ISBN 978 1407 11780 5

2 4 6 8 10 9 7 5 3 1

The right of Jim Eldridge to be identified as the author of this work has been
asserted by him in accordance with the Copyright, Designs
and Patents Act, 1988.

Prologue

I was born in a small hamlet in rural Shropshire, some five miles from Shrewsbury, in October 1830. My father was a Wesleyan preacher, and my mother was a Yorkshire woman, the daughter of a shoemaker. I had a sister two years younger than me, and two brothers, one older, one younger.

Although our life at home was comfortable, my father was a very strict man and drummed the teachings of the Bible into us at every opportunity. Every night, between eight and nine o'clock, we had family worship. The curtains were drawn, the candle was lit, and each of us children had to kneel separately at prayer, and then go to bed. On Sundays we had to go to church twice, and twice again during the week, on Tuesdays and Fridays, for, according to my father, we were all born wicked and in need of redemption.

Alas, instead of making me more god-fearing and church-minded, all this drumming-in of prayers and worship only made me resent it, and drove me away from the church and the very idea of religion. Unfortunately, I was a boy who liked playing games and having jokes with my sister and brothers. I never did anything cruel, just rough and tumble and the sort of tricks that all boys play. But in my father's eyes I was wayward and wild.

This view of me as wicked and sinful was also held by my grandfather. My grandfather was quite wealthy, owning a good deal of property that was expected to come to our family when he died and be shared amongst us.

In 1839, my grandfather accidentally drowned. When his will was read it showed the extent of his dislike for me: all his property was left to my father, except for four houses, which were left to my brothers and sister, to be theirs when they reached the age of 21. I was not mentioned anywhere in his will.

This deeply upset me. At the age of eight I had been labelled as wicked by my grandfather. This led to further rows between me and my father, resulting finally in his giving me a severe beating after he had been told I had threatened to burn our house down. I had not meant this, of course, they were only words spoken in anger following an argument between me and my brothers, but my father beat me hard for them. This was the first time he had ever physically chastised me, and I realized it would not be the last. His heart had hardened against me. From now on all there would be for me at home would be more Bible study, more prayers, all intended to drive the sinfulness out of me. So, at the end of May 1840, at the age of nine, I decided to run away. I took four sovereigns I had saved, and a shirt, and walked the five miles to Shrewsbury, where I caught a coach to London.

Chapter One

London, the great city! The maze of streets and alleyways, the huge numbers of people, the towering buildings, all this was bewildering to me after the fields and the slow pace of life in the country lanes of Shropshire.

I got down from the coach at Trafalgar Square, a vast area being built to commemorate the great victory over the French by our navy under Lord Nelson. Hundreds of men were at work, masons and builders, hauling stones. We had heard about this great square even as far afield as Shropshire. In fact, my father had written one of his sermons about it, and the Battle of Trafalgar, about duty to one's King and Country. I remember him making us sit and listen to him reading it to us in the parsonage before he went to church and read it to his congregation. I must have been only about six years old at the time, because at that time we still had a King, King William IV. Soon after he read his sermon in church, the King died and his niece, Victoria, succeeded him and my father had to change his sermon to talk about duty to Queen and Country. I remember he seemed upset about a woman being on the throne of England, but then he added bits to his sermon about Queen Elizabeth and the Golden Age, and that seemed to make him feel better.

With my small bag beside me containing my few meagre possessions, I stood at the south side of the square, looking at the work going on, at the men sweating and straining and hauling cement and stones. I had heard that in the middle a giant column was to be built, with a statue of Lord Nelson himself at the top. But right at this moment it was a building site. Still, it left an enormous impression on me, a boy of nine.

My first task was to find a place to stay. I had some money left in my pocket after paying my fare on the coach from Shrewsbury, but not much, so I had to be careful with it until I could find a way to raise some more. I had heard that there was work aplenty in London, and that the streets of the city were paved with gold. But the people who said this were those who had never set foot farther than Shrewsbury. I decided to find the cheapest lodgings.

As our coach had come from the west, and then southwards into the city, I had seen many great houses and parks, but nowhere that offered a place to stay at a price I could afford. So I decided to head east from Trafalgar Square, enquiring for lodgings on the way.

My route took me along a wide street called the Strand. Even as I entered it, I knew at once I would not find cheap lodgings here. On either side of the Strand were expensive-looking shops, and most of the people who thronged it wore fine rich-looking clothes. The wide cobbled roadway was filled with traffic: large dray carts loaded with barrels and pulled by huge heavy cart horses battling for a clear road between the horse drawn hansom cabs and omnibuses. The result of all those horse drawn vehicles was a mass of horse manure spread across the wide road. I was amused to see the people in their fine clothes, especially the women with their long wide dresses, making for the places where the road sweepers had cleared a path across the road for them so they could cross from one side of the Strand to the other. Sweeping aside the horse dung with their brooms was a never-ending job. I noticed that most of the sweepers were children about the same age as myself, some even younger. All of them looked ragged and filthy, and were barefoot. They swept the dung aside as the rich people crossed, and then held out their hand at the far side of the road for payment. I noticed that some stopped in the middle of the road and held out their hands for money, and guessed that they had been cheated before once too often, with people refusing to pay once they had got to the other side.

I walked on, past the shops with their windows filled with expensive clothes and jewellery and furniture and sweet things, and left the Strand behind as I entered Fleet

Street, and then on into Ludgate. Here, the buildings still looked expensive and grand, and the people well dressed, but there were fewer women in this area. Mainly it was men, hurrying to and fro, most of them dressed for official business in their dark frock coats, top hats and with silk cravats around their necks. I realized that this was the area known as the City, where the banks and counting houses held sway, and reckoned any lodgings here would be too dear for my taste. If I was to find somewhere reasonable to stay, I had to move away from these rich streets. To do that, I followed my nose.

I was looking for a different smell than that of horse dung: people.

In the towns in Shropshire where I came from there were areas where the poor lived, crammed into hovels and tiny cottages in mazes of streets and alleys. In these areas the smell was of overcrowded and unwashed bodies, of urine and excrement from open drains and cesspits, and rotting food scavenged by dogs. And cabbage being boiled, which seemed to be the main diet of the poor.

I turned off the main street and away from the well-to-do area, and soon found myself in a tangle of alleyways, with houses so close to one another on opposite sides of these alleys that their upper parts were almost touching. Here the dung dropped by horses was left mainly unswept. Open drains ran alongside the cracked

7

pavements at the edges of the uneven cobbled roadways, and the stench from them filled my nostrils. Many of the buildings were blackened with soot. Here, there were no grand ladies in fine wide dresses that draped along the ground as they walked, or gentlemen with high collars and top hats. Instead, the people wore ragged clothes and their faces were grimy from soot and a lack of washing, and most of them were bowed down under the weight of bundles of rags, or other articles of business.

Because I had grown up wild, as my father often complained, I had spent time in the poorer areas in Shropshire and knew how the people lived there, so I took care to make sure I did not stand out in this place. I removed my boots and hid them in my bag and went barefoot. Not only because it helped me blend in with the other children around, but I knew that a boy with boots might well be attacked and have them stolen. A good pair of boots can fetch a handy price.

My clothes were already crumpled and stained from my long coach journey, so I felt that I fitted right in. And I did, until I opened my mouth. At the first place I asked if there was a cheap room to rent, the woman looked at me puzzled, and then asked me to repeat what I had said. I realized that she had difficulty with my accent, but then I had difficulty understanding her as well, which was rough and thick and very unlike the voices of the poor people where I was from. However, although she didn't have any rooms to let herself, she pointed me around the corner to where she thought a neighbour of hers, a Mrs Crust, might have space for me.

Mrs Crust's house was a tiny building, all shaky and bent, and looked to me as if it was held up by the houses on either side. Mrs Crust herself was much the same as her house, rickety and bent, and with a crooked but kindly smile. I told her I was just arrived in London from the country. I also told her I was an orphan. Although it wasn't true, I didn't want to take the chance of her making enquiries about me or offering to send messages back to my family in Shropshire. My guess was that when my father found I was gone he would wash his hands of me. But on the other hand, he might report me as a runaway, and then people would be looking for me. So it was safest to tell Mrs Crust my parents were dead and I had no living family, and not to tell her my real surname, which was Kenton. Instead I told her I was called Dick Maybury, and I would be Dick Maybury ever after.

Mrs Crust had a kind and welcoming soul. "I'm sure I can fit in another young 'un," she said with a twinkle in her eye. She gestured me in, and I followed her up the stairs, which were all rickety, just like the rest of the house, and dusty and with cobwebs everywhere, up to the top landing. She pushed open the door to a small room, inside which were two beds and not much space for any other piece of furniture.

"I've got two young gentlemen not much older than you in here already," she said. "But you, being small, I'm sure we can make you comfortable on a mattress." And she reached under one of the beds and heaved out a lumpy mattress stuffed with straw. "There," she said. "You'll be snug in here."

She told me her terms, which seemed reasonable to me. I knew I had enough money in my purse to pay for three weeks' rent, and I was sure that during that time I would find work, or a way to make some money. I was set on making enough money so that I didn't have to share this tiny cramped room for very long.

Chapter Two

That night I met the two other boys who lived in that small room. The first to arrive was John Jarvey, who was twelve years old, and at first looked put out to find me in the room, but then he settled down when he saw that I was to have the straw mattress on the floor and not one of the two beds. I had a pie that I'd bought from a street vendor, and I let him have a piece to eat, which made him feel even happier about me moving into the room. But I was careful to tell him that this pie was my last food, so he didn't go searching through my bag while I was asleep to see if I had anything else. I was also careful to make sure I left a piece of pie to give to the other boy.

This turned out to be a good idea, as the other boy, who was called Daniel, was bigger and tougher than John, and he fixed me with a hard stare as he came into the room. Once he was eating the piece of pie I gave him he became a bit friendlier.

Because I didn't want them to think I was soft and could be bullied, and always be supplying them with food, I made up a story about my background. I told them I was an orphan who'd been forced to leave my home town after I'd beaten and nearly killed a boy during an argument. I said the police had a warrant for me if I ever went home, but I made Daniel and John swear to secrecy that they wouldn't tell my tale to Mrs Crust, or anyone else, in case word of my being here got back to the authorities. They both seemed to take my story seriously and nodded and swore they wouldn't tell on me, and I thanked them for that. When you are young and small like I was then – I always had been small for my age – you have to use tricks if you are going to survive in this hard world.

My story about having nearly killed another boy back home seemed to work with them, because they didn't try and bully me or steal my belongings. Maybe they wouldn't have anyway, but I'd already learnt in my young life that it doesn't do to take chances.

I spent the next week looking for work, but the work there was on offer didn't seem very attractive to me. I'd spent my life in a country parsonage, so I wasn't used to the sort of hard work that poor children like John and Daniel had put up with.

John worked for a rag-and-bone man, sorting through rubbish and making bad stuff into good so it could be sold on. It meant lots of heavy work carrying bales of rags into the shop, and hauling bits of metal and ornaments from buildings after they'd been broken up.

Daniel was training to be a slaughterman. At the moment he was just handling the sheep that came into the slaughterhouse and carrying the buckets of blood to the butchers, where it was turned into black puddings and other food. One day he took me with him to show me the slaughterhouse, which wasn't far away from our lodging house. It was a hideous place, smelling of blood and urine and sheep's droppings. The lower part of the walls and the floors were thick with blood and fat. Daniel showed me the underground room where sheep were thrown in from the street so that they'd break their legs and couldn't escape before they were killed and then cut up.

The stench and the whole atmosphere of the slaughterhouse was overpowering and although Daniel said he'd try and find me a job there, and I thanked him, I swore to myself that I would never want to work in that dreadful place, no matter how much the wages were.

As the days passed I became aware that the jobs on offer to me as a child were limited. All of them were menial dirty jobs: sweeping the roads of horse dung, as I'd seen children do on my first day walking along the Strand, or working as a mudlark. Mudlark was the name given to children, and adults, who went down to the River Thames at low tide and scavenged in the mud, looking for precious things that might have been brought to the mud through the sewers. The hope was to find jewellery or coins, but mostly they picked up lumps of coal, or old nails or bits of bone, which they sold to a rag-and-bone man, like John's boss.

When I hadn't found any work that suited me by the end of the first week, John suggested I be trained as a chimney sweep's boy.

"You're just the right size for it," he said. "You're small enough to go up the chimneys."

I nodded and smiled politely at him, as if I was seriously considering it, but in my head I was definitely rejecting it. I had known a boy back in Shropshire who was a chimney sweep. His skin was always black from the ingrained soot, and time and time again I saw his hands and knees bandaged from where he had been burnt on the hot bricks inside the chimney. Often he had been sent up a chimney to clean it when there had been a fire burning in the hearth just a few hours before.

After two weeks, my money was running out. The tone of Mrs Crust's voice became more anxious now when she asked me if I'd had any luck in finding a job.

"Only I can't have you staying here if you ain't got the money to pay your rent, Dick," she said, sadly but firmly.

"I'll have the money to pay my rent, Mrs Crust," I promised her. "It should only be a few days more, and then I'm sure I'll find something."

She gave me a look that showed her unhappiness. "You may not like what I say, Dick, but people like us can't afford to be too choosy in this life," she said. "The upper classes, the aristocracy and the clergy and the like, they can pick and choose. People from our walk of life, we have to take what's offered."

I had to hide my smile at my father, a clergyman, being described as "upper class". Although he may have had the status in our village, he didn't have the money. My mother had to scrape and mend to keep us children clothed.

"Like Daniel at the slaughterhouse, and John at McCready's shop, it may be hard and dirty work, but it's honest, and it pays the bills."

But I want more than just to pay the bills, I thought. I want smart clothes and to be able to buy good things from those expensive shops. I want to be able to ride in a smart carriage, with servants to help me down, and to arrange my clothes for me, and prepare me good luxurious food. And I won't get it by slaughtering sheep, or working at a rag-and-bone yard.

Chapter Three

It was during my third week in London that things changed for me. I was down to the last few pennies, and with no hope of finding a job that would fill my purse in a comfortable way. My rent was due. In an effort to make myself feel better, I'd walked to the Strand. That street made me feel rich, even though I was as poor as a church mouse. I'd walked along this street a few times since I'd arrived in London, hoping against hope that I'd see a sign outside one of the shops saying "Boy wanted" and get myself a job here, but so far that hadn't happened.

Usually, I walked home from the Strand along the wide street itself, or I went north up the side streets to the fruit and vegetable market in Covent Garden in the hope of snaffling myself a piece of fruit without the stall owners seeing me. But they watched out for boys like me, penniless waifs and strays, knowing our fingers were eager to grab something without paying, and I usually left as hungry as when I went.

Today, for a change, I decided to go south and explore the streets between the Strand and the River Thames. My hope was that trying somewhere new I might come across a business looking for a boy to work there. A clean business, not a slaughterhouse, or a rag-and-bone yard, or a soot store. And that was how I found the boys and the prison van which was their home.

The area is called the Adelphi and was mainly very large houses in blocks that went right down to the river. Once upon a time they had obviously been very grand, and some of them still were, but others looked the worse for wear, especially as I neared the river. Some of the blocks of houses had courtyards, which you entered through a high archway, and I saw that through the archway of one of the blocks was what looked like a prison van, but without wheels. Sitting outside the van was a gang of boys. Who were they? Gypsies?

"What d'you want?" growled a voice behind me, and I spun round to see a tall boy a couple of years older than I was, glaring at me.

"Er-n-nothing," I stammered. The boy kept glaring at me. I forced a smile and turned and gestured at the old prison van. "I was curious at seeing that, that's all."

"Better to see one like that, than a new one from the inside," chuckled another boy's voice. And now, from out of the shadows of the arches, stepped another, this one smaller and younger-looking than the tall one who'd glared at me. He smiled and held out his hand. "My name's Joe. What's yours?"

I took his hand and shook it. "Dick," I said. "Dick Maybury."

Joe looked me up and down, and then gave a sniff. "You don't look like you're doing too well for yourself, Dick," he said. "No money?"

I shook my head. "None at all," I said, and looked sorrowful. The truth was, I still had a couple of pennies left in my purse, but I wasn't going to tell this boy that. The bigger one certainly looked the sort who'd take them off me, and then throw my body in the Thames.

Joe stood, regarding me, as if weighing something up in his mind. Even though he'd smiled and shaken me by the hand, I was nervous. On the street a smile and a handshake meant nothing.

"What's up, Joe?" called one of the boys by the prison van.

"Don't know yet!" called back Joe. Then he looked at me and asked: "You interested in earnin' some money?"

I nodded. "Yes," I said.

Joe turned and looked at the older boy. "What d'you think, Abel?" he asked.

Abel hesitated, then nodded. "Worth a try," he said. "See what Larry says."

Joe shrugged. "This part ain't up to Larry." He slapped me on the shoulder in a friendly manner. "Come and meet the rest of the boys."

I followed Joe to the boys and the van, with Abel walking behind me. Some of the other boys had got up now and watched us, their expressions curious, while the others just stayed where they were and looked on. There were about ten of them, including Joe and Abel. We reached the old prison van and Joe gestured to the wooden steps.

"Sit yourself down, Dick," he said. "Let's hear your story."

I sat down and told them my story. Or, at least, I told them the story I'd told Mrs Crust, and Daniel and John. The boys listened.

When I'd finished, Abel nodded. "Seems all right to me," he announced.

"Course it does," grinned Joe. Then he shook me by adding, "but that's all it is – a story. Right, Dick?"

When I didn't answer straight away but stared back at him, shocked, he just grinned even more broadly and shook his head.

"It don't matter," he said. "None of us are who we think we are. We've all got our own stories. But here…" and now his tone turned firm, and he patted the side of the old wooden van "… we're true to one another."

"That's right," grunted a red-haired boy, his eyes watching me intently.

"You think you can be true to us, Dick?" asked Joe.

"If not, you can get on your way now," snapped the red-haired boy.

19

"Now now, Patrick," chided Joe. "There's no need to be inhospitable. After all, he don't know what the work is yet, do he?"

"Is it clean?" I asked.

Another of the boys, this one with long black hair that hung down to his shoulders, laughed. "Is it clean?" he mimicked me.

"Notice he didn't ask if it was legal," laughed Joe.

"It's very clean," nodded another boy. "You won't find cleaner."

Joe stood looking at me thoughtfully. Finally, he said, "You didn't say anything when I said you hadn't asked if it was legal."

I looked back at him, equally squarely in the face. "No," I replied firmly. "I didn't."

"You've never really been in trouble with the law before?" he asked.

"No," I said.

"And you ain't got no family?" asked Patrick, his tone suspicious.

"I ain't got no family," I said.

"Where do you live?" asked the tall boy, Abel.

I took a chance. I pointed at the old prison van. "Here. With you. If you'll have me," I told them.

Joe laughed out loud, and turned to the others. "See? Just like I thought!" he announced. "He's one of us!"

"He'd better be," said Patrick, still looking at me with suspicion in his eyes. "If he ain't and he peaches us, I'll slit his throat." And he produced a wicked-looking knife, which he held delicately in his hand, as if he considered throwing it at me. I looked back at him, defiantly.

"No need for that, Patrick," said Joe. "Put it away. Larry wouldn't like blood shed, it might stain his precious goods."

"Who's Larry?" I asked.

"You'll meet Larry soon enough," said Joe. "Right now, let's take young Dick here inside and find him a berth. Tomorrow, he can come to work with us and we'll see how he shapes up."

Chapter Four

Of course, I knew they were thieves as soon as I met them. The only things I didn't know were: what did they steal? Was it anything and everything, or did they deal in something particular? And, if they were thieves, as I suspected, how were they able to live so freely, here in this old derelict broken-down prison van, not far from a bustling street like the Strand, and so near all these grand houses? Why hadn't they been arrested?

They gave me the answers that night, as we sat outside the van in the gathering gloom. They'd already shown me what they specialized in: gentlemen's silk handkerchiefs. They had them stored, all neatly folded, in a box hidden beneath the floorboards of the van.

"We steal 'em and Larry buys them from us for ninepence each," Joe told me.

Ninepence! For just one handkerchief! At the slaughterhouse where Daniel worked, the fully-trained slaughterers only got fourpence for every sheep they killed!

"Mind, it's a bargain," said Finlay, the boy with the long

black hair. "In the shops in the Strand and along Regent Street, one of these can cost four shillings. Sometimes five."

I recalled seeing the well-dressed gentlemen walking along the Strand, taking pinches of snuff and then blowing their noses into their silk handkerchiefs. Taking snuff was all the fashion amongst gentlemen, which meant there were a lot of handkerchiefs about.

"And sometimes they don't tuck 'em back into their pockets properly," nodded Joe. "Usually on account of they want to be able to pull it out quick and blow."

"And that's where we come in," said Finlay with a sly grin. "You see a wipe hanging out of a pocket, and … snap! You grab it."

Wipes was another name for handkerchiefs.

"But carefully," warned Joe. "It's gotta be done gently, without the mark feeling he's being tugged."

"What about the constables?" I asked.

I didn't mind stealing in the way that Joe and the others outlined. There was no violence, and the gentlemen the handkerchiefs were taken from could well afford to buy another. But at the back of the mind there was that nagging shadow of prison, and even transportation, which meant being sent to one of the prison colonies in Australia.

The boys didn't seem bothered by the mention of the Law.

"The constables don't touch us," murmured Patrick.

"Thanks to Larry," chuckled Finlay. He winked at me and rubbed his finger and thumb together.

Joe shook his head, his expression serious. "You don't want to get too confident, lads," he warned them. "Larry can put money in the constables' pockets to look the other way, or take a wrong turning when they chase us, but if you're grabbed by a customer there's nothing he can do."

"He can get us off," said Abel. "The constable don't have to charge us."

"He does if the customer insists," said Joe firmly. "Remember Sharkey?"

At this the other boys fell silent and looked down at the ground, or exchanged awkward looks.

"Sharkey had it coming to him," muttered Abel. "He got careless."

"And it sounds to me like you lot are getting careless as well," warned Joe. He wagged his finger at them.

"We don't take chances!" He indicated me and added, "Like, we don't let Dick loose until he's seen how we work, and until his fingers are ready. Right now, I reckon we ought to turn in," he said gesturing at the old prison van. "We've got a busy day tomorrow, and Larry said he'd come by first thing to pick up the goods." He got up and went in, the other boys following. I joined them and found my berth, squeezed on a bench between Finlay and Patrick.

I wondered what Mrs Crust would say when I never came back to her house that night. Luckily for her, I'd paid my rent in advance so she was two days to the good. At least I wouldn't have that on my conscience. Unlike the gentlemen with their silk handkerchiefs, Mrs Crust couldn't afford to lose a penny. And she'd taken me in and given me a bed when I needed a roof over my head. Possibly, one day, I'd see her again. Maybe when I was rich. Until then, I was part of this gang. The gang of thieves.

The next morning I met Larry for the first time. I don't know what I'd expected. Someone rough-looking, maybe. Tough. A hardened criminal. What I hadn't expected was a gentleman: tall, thin, dressed in very neat and expensive black clothes, with a top hat and a dark red silk choker. He was clean-shaven, with very neat hair oiled back from his thin pale face. He was waiting for me outside the old prison van as I came down the rickety steps. He didn't offer to shake hands, he just inclined his head towards me in a nod of greeting.

"So you are Dick," he said. "Our new boy."

"Yes, sir," I replied.

He nodded again thoughtfully, and then said, "Let me explain the rules of your employment to you, Dick. This van you are living in is mine. I own it. The merchandise you bring me is mine. If you should acquire a piece of merchandise and take it to some other person rather than me, I shall be very displeased. You will be turned out of the van. You may also very likely be arrested and tried for theft and sent to prison, possibly even transported. If you are stupid enough to be caught," he continued, "you will not mention my name. If you do, you will suffer serious harm. Do you understand me so far?"

I nodded. "Yes, sir."

"Good," he said. He turned to Joe and patted him on the shoulder. "Joe is in charge here. He reports to me. If he gives me a bad report about you, you will leave the van. Is that clear?"

Once again, I nodded and said, "Yes, sir."

"Good," he said. "I hope you turn out to be a good worker." Then he turned to Joe. "Let's see the latest," he said.

Joe jerked a thumb at Abel, who went into the van, and came out a short while later with a stack of handkerchiefs, neatly folded one on top of the other. He held them while Larry inspected and counted them.

"Very good," said Larry at last, and he produced some cloth from an inside pocket, which he unfolded and I saw that it was a bag. He put the loot into his bag, then counted out the money into Joe's hands, while the other boys watched with greedy eyes.

"I will see you in a few days," he said. "Be fruitful in your work, and be careful."

With that he turned and walked away through the arch. Immediately, the other boys began clamouring for their money.

"Wait!" Joe commanded them sharply.

They stopped their hubbub, and Joe began to count their money out; the boys who had lifted the most got the most money.

When that was done, Joe put his own money into his pocket, and then grinned.

"Right, boys," he said. "Let's get to work!"

Chapter Five

I had expected the gang to head up to the Strand, where the rich gentlemen walked with their wives and sweethearts, but instead they headed down towards the river, and soon I found myself with them outside the Adelphi Station, which was the quay where the Thames steamboats arrived to unload their passengers and take on new ones. I was stunned to see so many people battling like stampeding cattle to get on and off the boats.

"This here's the best place," whispered Joe. "They're in a hurry, see."

"Where have they all come from?" I asked, awed at the sight of so many people. "Where are they all going?"

"Woolwich and Greenwich, mostly," said Joe. "Though some travel from as far away as Gravesend, and even Margate and Ramsgate. It's busy traffic. They reckon there are about fifteen thousand people a day travelling by steamboat along the Thames."

Fifteen thousand! I was stunned at the thought of that many people, and at that many boats!

As we watched, I saw Finlay and Patrick at work, moving

into the crush of passengers, and I saw what Joe meant. With the people pressing against one another like this, eager to get a place on board a boat, it was relatively easy for the boys to take hold of the corner of a handkerchief, and then just let the passenger move onward, leaving it caught between the boy's fingers. Time and time again it looked as if the boys were going to be pushed forward right up to the boat, and to the ticket inspector waiting on the quay, but just at the last moment they pulled back, and then drifted backwards through the crowds until they were out of the crowd.

I noticed that after the boys had snaffled only one wipe, two at the most, they withdrew and joined Joe and only went back into the fray after a decent interval. Meanwhile, their places had been taken by two others of the gang who went to work, fingers snatching and holding, until another piece of silk was in their grasp and stashed safely away in a pocket.

"It doesn't do to get too greedy," explained Joe. "Sometimes the steamboat companies put people on the watch for pickpockets. If they see a boy hanging about too long, they get suspicious."

And so it went on: when the crowds thinned out after a steamer had departed, the boys withdrew to stand and wait until the crowd had thickened again.

After a while, Joe gave a signal, and the boys left the

crowd and headed back towards the old prison van. I noticed they walked solo or in pairs, never as a gang, set on not attracting unwelcome attention.

When we assembled at the van, the boys began taking the handkerchiefs from their pockets and handing them to Joe, who pulled out a pad of paper and began making marks against each boy's name, and I realized that was how he knew how to apportion Larry's money.

"We'll give it a while, then we'll go back later this afternoon," Joe announced to the gang. "No sense in taking chances." He turned to me and asked, "Well, Dick? D'you think you could do that?"

"Yes," I nodded.

"In that case, you'd better get some practice in."

And so there, in that courtyard, I began to practise for my career as a thief and pickpocket. The boys took turns at leaving a piece of cloth dangling from their pockets, and walking about, while I attempted to tug it free without them noticing. It was harder than it had looked watching the others do it at the steamboat station. Just when my fingers were about to grab it, the boy would suddenly twist and move, and it would be snatched away from me. Once my hand was caught in Abel's painful grip as I felt in his pocket.

"That hurt!" I complained, holding my crushed fingers.

Abel looked at me and grinned. "You left your hand there too long."

"Because it was deeper inside his pocket," I countered. "It took longer to try and get hold of it."

"Exactly," said Joe. "So if that's the case, leave it. Grab the easy ones."

We carried on practising for the rest of the afternoon, until Joe said: "Enough now, time to go back to work."

I felt a sick feeling deep in my stomach at the realization that I was about to go into action! Joe must have seen the look of panic that passed over my face, because he added quickly, "Not you, Dick. Not yet. We'll leave you till tomorrow." He turned to Finlay and Patrick. "You two carry on practising with Dick, let him get the feel of it."

Patrick scowled. "Why should I lose money helping him practise," he demanded, "when I could be earning this afternoon?"

"Because Larry wants him to be good at it before he starts," said Joe. "And it's your turn. You and Finlay."

Patrick scowled again, then shrugged. "Come on, let's get you good."

That night, lying in my berth amongst the gang in the old prison van, I could hardly sleep. Panic kept rising up inside me. My father thought of me as wicked and sinful. Yes, I'd done some silly damage as a boy, smashed a gate and broken a window or two – but it was never on purpose.

They were usually accidents while I was playing about. Now, I was going to commit a crime. I was going to be a thief. My throat felt dry at the thought of it. Would I get caught? In my imagination I felt a hand grabbing my collar and heard the shout of "Thief!" I saw myself being grabbed and dragged into a police van and taken to Newgate Prison. As I lay there in my berth, I felt myself shaking, and I had to grip myself tight to stop. I hoped none of the other boys noticed. I needed them to believe in me. I needed to believe I could do it. I needed to be strong.

Chapter Six

The gang trooped down to the Adelphi Station, where already the passengers waiting to get on board a boat were herded together like cattle.

"Right," whispered Joe. "You go in with Abel, Dick. And remember, for starters, only take wipes that are hanging out enough for you to get a grip on it without dipping into a pocket. No sense in getting caught on your first day."

I nodded, then Abel and I moved forward into the crowd, and straight away I felt I was in danger of being suffocated or trampled underfoot. The crowd of people, most of whom were men, pushed forward to make sure they got onto the next available boat, and they pushed so much that there was barely space between them for me to be able to breathe, tiny as I was. I felt a sense of panic coming over me as I was squashed, my face pressed into a man's back. I pushed back sharply, but was pushed forward again, pressed into a tall man, and I found myself looking at the corner of a green silk handkerchief sticking out of the man's jacket pocket.

Joe had instructed me to keep my hands at chest height,

not down by my sides, so they would be ready to grab and lift without making anyone behind me suspicious by jabbing them with my elbows if I raised my hands. I took the corner of the green silk between my finger and thumb. I was pressed so close against the man that I was sure no one behind me could see my hand. Suddenly there was a shout of "Ready to board!" and the crowd gave a surge forward. As they did so I jostled to stay where I was, took a small pace back and there I was, holding the wipe. Hastily I stuffed it inside my jacket, into the small pocket there, and then pushed forward again, as if I was battling to get to the boat.

I remembered Joe's instructions. One wipe will do. No more than two at a time, otherwise you're in danger of being spotted.

The crowd was parting now, heading to one side of the quay to let the newly arrived passengers off the steamboat. I kept to the side of the crowd waiting, and then, as the incoming passengers pushed their way through, I joined them and let myself be swept along the quay until I was back with Joe and the other boys.

I produced the green silk from my inside pocket and handed it to Joe, who smiled as he took it and dropped it into his bag.

"Well done, Dick," he said. "Now go and get another one."

I nodded, and returned to the fray. Once again, getting right into the middle of the crush, I scanned the jackets of the people around me, looking for the edge of a handkerchief. This time it took me longer to spot one, most men seemed to have pushed theirs down into their pockets. Obviously word had spread that pickpockets were operating. I spent about ten minutes being jostled backwards and forwards by the crowd, being pushed and pushing back, before I spotted the decorated edge of another wipe, a red one this time, just poking out from a pocket, a few men away. I pushed myself through and positioned myself behind the man and waited for the surge of the crowd moving forward. When it came, I was ready. I managed to grab the edge of the red silk, ready for the next surge to leave it in my grasp. But the next surge never came! There was obviously some sort of hold-up, and I found myself pinioned with my arm trapped and my fingers holding on to the material. If anyone looked down at me now, I would be caught for sure! I released my fingers from the handkerchief, but I couldn't move my trapped arm, which left my fingers still poised very suspiciously over the man's pocket. Please don't anyone look at me, I prayed silently. Please don't anyone look!

Suddenly the man in front of me moved forward. At the same time I felt the man behind me shove me hard in the back. I stumbled forward, bumped into the man in front, who ignored me, but I took the chance and grabbed the edge of the red wipe in his pocket once again, and as I did there was another surge forward by the crowd. I sidestepped, and then pushed sideways. In my hand I held the piece of silk! Two handkerchiefs at ninepence each meant eighteen pence, one shilling and sixpence!

I forced my way back through the crowd and reached Joe. He could see from the pleased expression on my face that I'd been successful.

"Well done, Dick," he complimented me, taking the wipe and putting it into his bag. "Two in a short time. You are a natural!"

After that first day, I even began to enjoy it. It was the challenge, seeing how many I could lift in a day. Joe had warned us all about not taking too many, otherwise if the number of complaints got too big the constabulary would have to act and arrest somebody, no matter how much Larry paid them to look the other way. But either I got bigheaded, or I got greedy, and one day – after I'd been with the gang for two weeks – I took four, one after the other, in one go. Joe was furious.

"Are you trying to get us all pinched!" he shouted at me as I handed them to him in the cover of the wharf.

"I thought you'd be pleased," I said. "Larry will be."

"It won't be Larry going to jail!" retorted Joe. "In future, no more than two at a time, otherwise you're out of the gang!"

I was upset and annoyed at Joe's attitude. I had shown how good I was, but instead of being pleased he was angry and had shouted at me in front of the other boys. So I decided if I was going to be limited to two at a time, I would set myself other challenges to make it more of a game. Instead of just taking the easy ones, I decided to develop my skill as a pickpocket by dipping my fingers into pockets.

I thought I could do this safely because of the crush of people around me. It just goes to show that if you are too smug, or too greedy, you are your own worst enemy. The first time I tried it I was lucky, I came up with one and went off feeling very pleased with myself. The second time I did it … I got caught!

Chapter Seven

The hand came from behind me and clamped on my wrist as I slipped my fingers into the pocket in front of me.

"Got you!"

The shout made my victim turn round. He saw the man gripping my wrist tightly.

"What's going on?" he asked.

"This little thief had his hand in your pocket," said my captor. His grip on my wrist tightened painfully.

"I didn't!" I blurted out.

"Yes you did! I saw you!"

The man's eyes narrowed and he hissed at me. "I've lost three handkerchiefs in the last six months at this station. Ever since the last one went I've been keeping my eyes peeled for the thief responsible!"

"It wasn't me!" I insisted. "I was just pushing to try and get on board the boat!"

"Which boat?" asked the man whose pocket I'd been trying to pick.

The question stumped me. Which boat? Frantically, I tried to remember the places that Joe had said the steamboats went to.

"Margate!" I said.

The man shook his head. "This boat doesn't go to Margate," he said.

"See!" cried the other man triumphantly. Then he called out, "Constable! Constable!"

That did it. I tried to wriggle out of his grasp and run away, but he had a vice-like grip on me. Frantically, I kicked at him, but being so tightly pressed in the crowd I couldn't get a proper kick in. My attempts to escape only made him tighten his hold on me even more.

Then I saw the uniformed figure of a constable pushing his way through the crowd, called by the rumpus. I wished and hoped that he was one of those Larry was paying to look the other way. If he was, even if he took me in charge, he'd let me go once we were out of the crowd. But my hopes were dashed as the man holding me said, "I've caught a pickpocket, and I insist on coming with you to the police station to give my evidence and make sure he's charged."

And that was that.

The constable took firm hold on my collar and the crowd parted to let us go through, with my captor following close behind. As we got to the edge of the crowd, I noticed that Joe and the rest of the gang had made themselves scarce. I was on my own.

The constable hustled me along the street and then across the Strand and towards Covent Garden, and I realized with a shock where we were headed. We were going to Bow Street, the police station and magistrates' court. As we walked, the man who'd caught me kept up with us, talking all the time about how he'd had his precious handkerchiefs stolen by pickpockets while waiting for a boat at the Adelphi Station, and how he hoped I'd get a heavy sentence to stop others doing it.

"Transportation, that's what ought to happen to him!" he continued. "Five shillings each those handkerchiefs cost me! Five shillings! And these scoundrels steal them without a thought! He should be flogged! And publicly!"

"I'm sure the magistrate will make the right decision, sir," said the constable.

As we crossed the Strand I wondered if I could get away. Maybe twist my way out of the constable's grip and run along the road, dodging in between the horses and cabs and omnibuses and wagons. There was a chance that neither the constable nor the gentleman would want to run after me and risk slipping in the horse manure that spread over the road. But, as if reading my thoughts, when we reached the Strand, the constable twisted my collar. He kept a firm grip on me with both hands all the way to Bow Street.

We marched through the doorway into the huge building, the constable pushing me towards the charge desk, where a uniformed sergeant stood. The sergeant looked down at me then up at the constable.

"Yes?" he asked.

"This gentleman here caught a pickpocket," announced the constable.

"And I'm here to be a witness at his trial!" snapped the man. "I want this young rascal to get what he deserves! A whipping! And jail!"

The sergeant nodded and opened up a ledger, then dipped a pen into an inkwell. "Right," he said, "let's have the details."

At that stage I knew I was really sunk. Even if the constable had been in the pay of Larry, once my crime had been entered into the book there was no hope for me. I was going to stand trial.

My details were taken, although all I was able to give them was my false name, Dick Maybury. I gave my address as Mrs Crust's lodging house, because I didn't want to have to face a charge of vagrancy too.

The man who'd caught me then gave his statement, and afterwards I was taken down to the cells.

Down beneath the police station it was dark and dank, with a strong smell of damp. A constable led me along a high-ceilinged stone corridor, and then handed me over to a turnkey, who unlocked a heavy metal door and thrust me inside.

There were two bunks in the cell. A man lay on one of them, snoring. His face was bruised and there was a cut of one side of his face, and a crusting of dried blood. He stank of drink and urine. I felt a sickness in the pit of my stomach. He looked the kind of man who lived by violence. What would happen to me when he woke up? Would he attack me, just for being there?

The turnkey went out and slammed the heavy metal door shut after him, and turned the key in the lock. It was the most mournful heart-breaking sound I'd ever heard. I sat down on the hard wooden bench, dropped my head into my hands, and thought of all that had happened to me since I ran away to London. The dirt and the poverty of the tiny room at Mrs Crust's house, the gang of boys at the old derelict prison van, and now locked up in Bow Street awaiting trial as a thief. My life had turned out exactly as my father had warned me it would.

Chapter Eight

Luckily for me, my cellmate wasn't as terrifying as I'd feared he would be. He was a drunk and he'd got his cuts falling over. He just lay on his bunk, either snoring, or moaning miserably to himself.

I was brought up before the magistrates the next morning. There were three of them on the bench, all old men wearing dark cloaks and glaring at me as I stood on tiptoe to try and peer over the top of the dock so I could see them and they could see me.

"Is there a box the accused could stand on, in order that we may see him?" demanded one of the magistrates.

This had obviously happened many times before, because a box was produced very quickly.

The clerk of the court said my name and then read the charge out: "Dick Maybury, on a charge of pickpocketing by the area known as the Adelphi Station."

The magistrate who was in the middle, who seemed to be the one in charge, asked, "How do you plead? Guilty or not guilty?"

"Not guilty," I said.

The magistrate studied me. "How old are you?" he asked.

"Nine years old, sir."

"And where are your parents?"

"I'm an orphan, sir."

"Do you have any family?"

"No, sir."

The magistrate turned to the clerk. "What are the facts of this case?" he asked.

The clerk read out the statement from my captor, and from the constable who arrested me.

"Are these witnesses here?" asked the magistrate.

"They are, your honour," said the clerk.

The constable was the first one called and he gave his evidence, which was the same as the statement the clerk had already read.

"Did the accused have any property on him that was identified as stolen?" asked the magistrate.

"No, your honour," said the constable.

"Because I caught him before he got the chance to take it!" came a roar from the man who'd made the charge against me.

The magistrate fixed the man with a glare. "This is a court of law. You will be silent, sir, until you are addressed," he said sternly. He then asked the constable a couple of other questions about what he had or had not seen, to which the

44

constable gave vague answers. Then the magistrate asked him: "Is this boy known to the police?"

"No, your honour," replied the constable. "There is nothing known against him."

Then my capturer took the witness stand. After taking the Bible in his right hand and swearing that he would tell The Truth, The Whole Truth and Nothing But The Truth, he gave his evidence: how he'd been watching me acting suspiciously, and then seen me dip my fingers into the gentleman's jacket pocket.

The magistrate turned to the constable. "Is the victim of this attempted robbery here?" he asked.

"No, your honour," replied the constable.

"Did you take his name and address?"

The constable looked uncomfortable. "No, your honour," he said.

On hearing this, the magistrate's lips tightened into a thin disapproving line.

"Very well," he said. "I find the case proved, but as nothing was actually taken, and in view of the fact that this is a first offence, I sentence the accused to two months' penal servitude at Westminster Bridewell. Take him down."

As the constable standing with me in the dock took hold of me to lead me away, I heard the man who caught me shout out angrily, "Just two months? He should be whipped! He should be transported!"

As I was led down the steps back to the cells, I heard the magistrate shout, "Silence! Any more of that and I'll have you charged with contempt of court. Next case!"

And so I went to prison.

Actually, I knew I'd been lucky and my fate could have been a great deal worse. A few years before stealing had been a capital offence, punishable by hanging. Even now it was often punished with transportation.

When the boys of the Adelphi gang and I had sat around the police van in an evening, we'd often talked about the things that might happen to us if we were ever caught. It was a form of bravado, and also a kind of fun. We swapped stories of people we knew that had been sent to prison or transported. Not that I had any such stories to tell because I was new to London, although I did have one story about a man in Shropshire who'd been sent to Australia for rustling sheep. He had been sentenced to ten years' hard labour there. If he came back to England before his sentence was up, he would be hanged.

The boys told me that men could no longer be hanged for this. Anyway, the reality was, once people got sent to Australia they never came back. It was too far, for one thing, the journey taking nearly half a year.

Those evenings we'd sat and talked about crime and punishments, various prisons had been mentioned:

which ones were hard prisons, which ones were soft, and I'd remembered that Patrick had described Westminster Bridewell as one of the soft ones. "My sister was in Westminster Bridewell," he'd told us. "She said it wasn't so bad. Mainly women and children. No murderers."

As I was loaded with the other prisoners into the prison van, I hoped that the place was as soft as Patrick had said it was.

Chapter Nine

It wasn't. Or, maybe it was in the eyes of Patrick's sister. To me, Westminster Bridewell was a horrible place. If there was a prison worse than this then I didn't want to have anything to do with it.

It was true that many of the prisoners were women, but the rest were boys under the age of seventeen. The wing where the boys were kept was violent and vicious, with the threat of beatings and kickings always hanging over us. Not from the warders, but from the inmates.

Most of the time we were kept locked up in our cells, and my cellmates were Matthew, a thug of fifteen who'd robbed a shopkeeper, and Poge, a thin nervous boy of thirteen who had nightmares every night and used to wet his bed. The situation was made worse because Matthew used to be woken up by Poge crying out in his sleep, and he'd beat and kick him to shut Poge up. This just made Poge cry out and wet himself all the more.

The few hours we were allowed out into the exercise yard during the day were even worse. Because Westminster Bridewell was seen as a "soft" prison, with no hardened and serious criminals, like murderers and forgers, there weren't enough prison guards on duty to keep a proper eye on the prisoners and those who were in the yard were not that bothered. So the bullies and thugs ruled the exercise yard and would often take someone out of sight from the guards and beat them for pleasure. Even though I did my best to keep a low profile and not bring myself to anyone's attention, it happened to me twice. The first time I lost two teeth, and the second time, near the end of my second month, I ended up in the prison hospital unconscious.

Neither time was anyone charged with attacking me. But then, I wisely kept my mouth shut about who had hurt me, because I knew if I said, I'd only get hurt much worse the next time. The first time I was beaten, the warders didn't even seem to notice. The next time, when I was carried unconscious to the prison hospital, the warders on duty had to report it, so it was written up as "fell while running".

During my two months in Westminster I had my tenth birthday, but I didn't tell anybody. What was the point? There was certainly nothing for me to celebrate. The only good thing to come from this experience was the knowledge that once I was out, I was never going back to prison again.

At the end of my two months, I was released. I only had one penny on me, which I'd managed to keep hidden. All the other money I'd come in with had been stolen from me by the other prisoners. As I walked out through the prison gates, I reflected that I was once again homeless and penniless, but now – at the age of ten – I was also a convicted criminal.

I was surprised to find two young men waiting for me as I came out of the Bridewell. They looked to be in their early twenties. Both wore smart clothes with top hats and greeted me with cheerful smiles and handshakes and greetings of "Welcome back, Dick!" and "It's good to see you!" I shook their hands, but looked back at them warily. "Who are you?" I demanded.

"My name's Charlie," said the thinner, fair-haired one, "and this is Michael." He pointed to his dark-haired companion, who was a bit chubbier.

"We're your new best friends," beamed Michael.

I shook my head. "No you're not," I said firmly. "You're trouble. I can tell." I jerked my thumb back at the Bridewell. "I've just come out of prison after serving two months and I don't intend to go back inside again."

"And you won't, Dick!" said Charlie, his tone assured and certain.

"We've got a proposition for you," added Michael.

"I'm not interested," I told them, and went to push past, but Michael took hold of my shoulder. Not with a harsh grip, gently, but firmly.

"All we want to do is talk to you for a bit," he said. "We'll buy you a cup of coffee and a meal while we tell you more about ourselves. If you don't like what we have to say, then you can just go on your way, and that'll be it. No hard feelings."

I studied them. They were obviously crooks of some kind, but they seemed genuine enough. And I didn't have anything worth stealing. Also, after two months in the Bridewell, it had been a long time since I'd drunk a good cup of coffee, or eaten a good meal. And I didn't have the money to buy them for myself.

"All right," I said. "I'll listen, but that's all."

"Good," beamed Charlie. "We hoped you'd say that. We've got a cab waiting."

And they walked me away from the entrance to the Bridewell round the corner, where a hansom cab was standing, with a beautiful chestnut horse between the shafts and the cabbie sitting on a box at the top. Once we were in, Charlie called up to the cabbie, "Whitechapel!" and the cab moved off.

I had to admit I was impressed. It was the first time I'd ever been inside a cab. The seats were made of soft leather and as comfortable as any I'd ever sat on. I sort of sank back into them. The inside of the cab smelled of leather and soap, and was clean and smart. Whoever these two were, and whatever their game was, there was obviously money to be made in it if they could afford to ride around London in a cab like this. But then I reminded myself that I'd just come out of prison only a few minutes ago, and I had no intention of going back in.

"So, what's the game?" I asked.

By way of answer, Charlie put his finger to his lips and gestured upwards, to where the cabbie sat atop the cab.

"Later," he said. "When we're somewhere it's safe to talk."

That place turned out to be a coffee house in Whitechapel, where Charlie and Michael were obviously well known because we were shown to a table at the back of the coffee house, shielded from the rest of it by a tall decorated wooden screen. Once we had our three cups of coffee placed before us and had ordered meals, they outlined their plans.

"We need a tooler," said Michael.

"What's a tooler?" I asked, puzzled.

Charlie and Michael exchanged looks, and then laughed.

"Well well, he's been working in London and he don't know what a tooler is," chuckled Charlie.

"That's because he's an innocent," said Michael.

"Yes I am," I said. "And I intend to stay that way from now on."

Michael and Charlie nodded, as if in understanding.

But then Charlie said, "So, what will you do for money, Dick? You're ten years old. You've got no family, so we hear. What sort of work is there for a boy like you in London?"

"Especially one who's just done two months in prison for theft," nodded Michael.

"Road crossing sweeper?" suggested Charlie. "Chimney sweep. Oakum picker."

"Or maybe you think it might be best to leave London altogether and start a new life somewhere else," said Michael. "But where? Another city? And doing what?"

"I can read and write," I told them defiantly. "I could get a job as a clerk."

The two exchanged looks.

"A clerk," repeated Michael, nodding. He turned back to me. "You're a bit young for that, Dick. And even when you're old enough, there's not a lot of money in being a clerk."

"Michael knows," put in Charlie. "His dad was a clerk."

"And we lived in two squalid rooms because my poor old Dad couldn't afford anything better. Is that what you want, Dick? Earning just enough to pay the rent on some squalid cramped little room, and doing the same job every day, day after day, with maybe one day off on Sunday to go to church, or sit in that same little room and watch your life go by?"

"And you've got to survive until you're old enough to

53

be a clerk," added Charlie. "That's years yet, Dick. Years of scratching a living. Sharing one cramped room with others if you're lucky, living on a factory roof in all weathers if you're not."

I thought of the tiny cramped and dirty room I'd shared with Daniel and John at Mrs Crust's house. I looked at Charlie and Michael with their fine clothes, drinking coffee at a private table in this coffee house, able to afford to ride in a cab with soft leather seats and I made my decision.

"What's a tooler?" I asked again.

They smiled, and then explained. A tooler was a pickpocket who picked ladies' pockets. "It's easy," said Michael. "We only target ladies who wear big skirts with pockets. With all those petticoats under them, they can't feel anything. You can dip your fingers into their pockets without them knowing it's happening, providing you're not too rough, of course."

I shook my head.

"It don't matter if they can feel me dipping or not, all it needs is someone to see me and raise the alarm," I scowled. "That's how I got caught before."

"Ah, but that's where this is different," said Charlie. "We put a shield between you and everyone else. Me and Michael and a few others. Tall men. We give you cover. We look smart, so anyone watching doesn't think anything's out of the ordinary."

Michael smiled. "As far as they're concerned, we might well be companions of the lady."

I sipped at my coffee and thought it over. "Why me?" I asked, after a while.

"Because we heard good things about you while you were with the Adelphi gang," said Michael.

"We liked the way you didn't say anything when you were arrested," added Charlie. "No names given. That's good. That shows character and trust."

"We need someone we can trust," said Michael.

"Plus, you're small for your age. For this game, we need someone small."

I studied them, still unsure. What they said seemed easy enough but then so had taking handkerchiefs down at the Adelphi Station, and I'd been caught doing that.

But then I thought about my alternatives: dirty, rough, hard work for little money, and squalid living conditions, just like they said.

"Very well," I said, nodding. "I'm in."

Chapter Ten

For the next three days I practised the art of tooling. Charlie and Michael had rooms at a house in Flower and Dean Street, in Spitalfields, in the East End.

At first I was surprised because Flower and Dean Street was a filthy area, with all manner of crooks and thieves living there. You could see that in some places there'd once been a small garden at the back of a tiny terraced house, but then another dwelling had been thrown up in the garden, squashed back to back with the original house. Most of these places were common lodging houses for some of the roughest people in London. This had happened all the way along Flower and Dean Street, with the result that it was one of the most crowded and smelliest places I'd ever experienced. It didn't fit with the smart way that Charlie and Michael dressed, and how they carried themselves, like upper-class gentlemen.

"The good thing about Flower and Dean Street, Dick," explained Charlie to me, "is that the police are too frightened to come anywhere here. In other words, we're safe. And, once we've got enough money to live respectable lives, we'll move."

Which made sense.

I was soon introduced to the rest of the gang, another young man called Stephen, who was as well dressed as Charlie and Michael, and a young woman called Emily. Emily, I discovered, was Charlie's sweetheart.

How the trick worked was this: Emily and Charlie would be out in the best parts of town, dressed in their fine clothes, and Michael and Stephen would be walking separately, two young gentlemen out for a stroll. They told me that I'd also be dressed up in good clothes, walking alongside them. If anyone noticed us they might think I was with Charlie and Emily, though Charlie and Emily could deny that afterwards if anything went wrong and say they'd never seen me before.

Charlie, Michael, Stephen and Emily were the "stalls", and Charlie was also "the stickman".

"When we've spotted a likely prospect..." began Charlie.

"Which is usually a lady standing still, looking into a shop window," interrupted Emily.

"I was gonna say that," said Charlie, a bit put out.

"Sorry," Emily apologized.

"When we've spotted a likely prospect," repeated Charlie, "which is usually like Emily says, we go into action. Me and Emily come up one side of the lady, and

57

Stephen and Michael come up on the other. You, Dick, will be with me and Emily, like we're all out together, like family. Once we're all in position, we close up around the lady, but making sure we don't push against her. The point is, with me, Michael, Emily and Stephen around you, you'll be hidden from view, so you can start dipping. Think you can do it?"

"Yes," I nodded keenly.

"Right," said Charlie. "Let's set to work."

Emily played the mark we were stealing from, while the others stood around her, and I slipped in between them so I was right up close to her.

Women in those days wore long wide dresses that went right to the ground, and flared out like a tent. They had lots of petticoats on, all of them stiffly starched. Beneath the petticoats women wore very tight and stiff stays and corsets to keep their waists looking small. Some of these corsets had bones, and they were tied with thick ribbons and strings. With all of that, it made sense what the gang said, that most ladies wouldn't feel a hand dipping into the pocket of their skirt. And, even if they did, they didn't take much notice, because with these very wide skirts they were always bumping against things or people, or being bumped against.

I gently fanned the surface of Emily's skirt to make sure the pocket had a purse in it, as Charlie told me. Then I poked my fingers in and very carefully took the purse out.

It was certainly a lot easier than taking handkerchiefs from gentlemen. Gentlemen's jackets were generally tighter about their body than ladies dresses and most men could feel anybody dipping them.

As soon as I got hold of the purse, I slipped it to the stickman, which was Charlie. In turn, Charlie passed it on to Michael. When we did the trick a second time, he passed it to Stephen. It always got passed on. This meant that if I was ever caught, there'd be no evidence, because the purse would have disappeared.

The stalls' job, as well as hiding me from sight, was also to keep a lookout for the police, or anyone who might recognize them and raise the alarm. If that happened and anyone spotted me picking the pocket, they had to create a diversion to confuse the situation.

"We also get in the way of anyone giving chase, while you run off as fast as you can and get away," said Michael.

"Once the trick's been done, we separate, and then we meet up later at an agreed rendezvous," Charlie said. "There, we check the takings and share out the spoils."

The gang showed me the sort of purses I was after. All of them were small, and either embroidered or made of a kind of lace. Charlie was very firm that, unless they were really valuable, empty purses and any objects that might be easily identified, had to be thrown away.

We did three days of practising in the rooms at Flower and Dean Street until the gang were all satisfied that I could do it swiftly and without fumbling. In this practice, the time I'd spent with the Adelphi gang taking handkerchiefs from gentlemen's pockets came in very useful. I'd developed a light touch, and, because I had small hands with thin fingers, it was easier for me to slip them inside a lady's pocket.

Then, on the fourth day, we went to work properly.

Charlie and Emily had got me a really smart outfit: a close-fitting black frock coat, black trousers, black cravat and a little beaver hat. I looked a little gentleman. Emily had a smart dress on, and Charlie, Michael and Stephen also looked perfect gentlemen, out for a stroll.

We went to St Paul's Churchyard. Charlie told me this was a perfect place for our trade: it was a centre where rich people went, with good and expensive shops, and at this time of day, which was mid-afternoon, there were quite a few wealthy-looking ladies mingling around. Charlie and Michael were in charge, and after studying the ladies for promising victims, they selected a woman standing looking into the window of a confectioner's shop. No words were said, just a flicker of the eyes from Charlie to me in her direction, and we were in action. She was on her own, which meant no companions to raise any alarm. We followed her until she stopped to look in the window of a hosier. Then the gang stopped and gathered around her, while pretending to look at the sights of St Paul's, and I set to work.

Just like the very first time I'd stolen a handkerchief with the Adelphi gang, I felt the rising panic and I could barely breathe, but I fought get myself under control. Above all, my hands must, or that could raise the alarm with the woman for sure, even with her stiff starched petticoats.

As it turned out, it was easy. Those three days of intense practice in the gang's rooms paid off, and I blessed Charlie and Michael for making me lift those different purses from Emily's skirt pocket, time after time after time. Immediately, I passed it to Charlie, who snaffled it and then passed it on, but I didn't see to whom, because by then we were moving again, Charlie and Emily heading in one direction, Michael and Stephen the opposite way. I turned and walked off, remembering Charlie's instructions: don't run. Don't even walk fast. Just stroll. Maybe look in a shop window, and then saunter off. Don't cause a fuss, don't attract attention to yourself.

In fact, it was the walking away that I found the most frightening part. The whole time I expected someone to shout out "Thief!" or "Stop that boy!" And even though I didn't have the purse on me, I didn't want to be grabbed and taken before the constabulary again. But there were

61

no shouts, no calls of alarm or panic, and I kept strolling until I was out of the grounds of the Churchyard. Then I made for our meeting point, a coffee house not far from St Paul's.

The others were already there. Emily and Charlie grinned broadly when they saw me.

"Here's our little hero," announced Charlie.

We went into a private room at the rear of the coffee house, and while Stephen ordered coffee, Charlie spilled the contents of the purse onto a table and counted the money. There was two pounds. For me, that was a small fortune.

Charlie divided the money equally into five piles, with eight shillings in each pile. Eight shillings all of my own! This was the most money I'd ever had in my life! But then Charlie wiped the delighted smile off my face by saying, "Sadly, Dick, there are deductions from your share, for those clothes you're wearing."

"But…" I began to protest.

"Good clothes cost money, Dick," said Charlie. "I've paid out for them already. And this won't work with you walking around looking like a ragamuffin. However, I'll just take some of the money back at this stage. We don't want you losing heart." With that, he took five of the eight shillings from my pile, leaving me three. He gave me a smile and a wink. "The more purses we lift, the sooner those clothes will be paid off."

"How much more is there to be paid off?" I asked suspiciously.

"Not much," replied Charlie. He turned to the others with his characteristic confident smile. "After we've had our coffee, we'll go to work some more and see what pickings we can find, and help Dick here pay off his debt quicker."

"Where to next, Charlie?" asked Emily.

"I thought we'd start at Newgate and work our way along to Cheapside," said Charlie. "We haven't done that beat in a while, so we might strike lucky there."

And, indeed, we did. By the time we returned to the rooms at Flower and Dean Street at five o'clock, we had taken another four purses! And this time my share cleared the money Charlie said I owed him for the clothes, with some left over. I jangled the coins in my pocket. For the first time in my life, I was rich!

Chapter Eleven

For the next two months we carried on the business. Under Charlie's direction we only went out twice a week, and never to the same place too often. "That's a sure way to get caught," said Charlie. "Leave it a few weeks before you go back to a place, otherwise they'll be watching out for you and recognize you."

Flower and Dean Street wasn't far from Mrs Crust's, and I suppose it was only to be guessed that sooner or later I'd run into either John or Daniel, or Mrs Crust herself. Sure enough, one day as I was walking along Whitechapel, I heard a voice call out "Dick!" I turned, and saw John Jarvey staring at me.

"Why, hello, John!" I greeted him.

He came along the pavement, his eyes and his mouth wide open as he took in the smart clothes I was wearing. I noticed that he was still wearing the same sort of patched old clothes he'd worn when we shared that room at Mrs Crust's.

"Why, Dick," he said, stunned. "Look at you and all your finery! Has someone died and left you money?"

I smiled and shook my head. "No. Just hard work."

He frowned, puzzled. "What sort of work?" he asked. "I work long hard hours and I could never afford to have clothes like that. And a hat like that, as well!"

"The clothes go with the job," I told him airily.

"But what sort of job is it?" he insisted. "Is it a bank?"

"Kind of," I said. "I got into partnership with a couple of swell young men whose business is money." I gave a chuckle. "The truth be told, John, I'm not as well off as I look. The men I work with say in our business we have to dress up and look right. So really it's all show."

John was an honest boy and I knew he wouldn't approve of my new profession. I changed the subject by asking about him and Daniel, and Mrs Crust.

"Daniel's got promotion at the slaughterhouse," said John. "He earns enough to have a room of his own, so now I'm sharing with another boy called Jack. He's all right, but I think he steals, so I have to keep my things close at hand."

I shook my head sadly. "A thief, eh," I sighed. "It's a bad thing when you can't trust the people you share a room with."

"Yes, but I'm hoping to be able to get a room of my own soon," said John, brightening up. "I've just found a new place at a pawnbroker's in Bishopsgate. I'm going to be paid ten shillings a week!" he announced proudly. "I start there next Monday."

"Well good luck to you, John," I said.

We shook hands and parted. As I walked away I couldn't help but reflect on our different financial circumstances. John was proud of earning ten shillings a week. I was making a lot more than that in just one day! All right, John didn't have the constant fear of going to prison, but he would work long hours for his money, six days a week. Me, I was my own master. Well, to an extent, so long as our gang stayed together. And as long as we didn't get pinched.

It was a couple of days after my meeting with John that we were sitting in the back room of our regular coffee shop in Whitechapel relaxing after a successful morning dipping. We'd lifted three purses and taken five pounds, which meant we had a pound each. Life was good.

"What happened to your last boy?" I asked, sipping my coffee.

"He got transported," said Emily.

Immediately an awkward silence fell over the table. Charlie gave Emily a glare. Emily looked back at him and gave an apologetic shrug.

"I'm sorry," she said. "I thought Dick knew."

"He does now," said Stephen, and he laughed, which broke the tension.

"No sense in hiding it," nodded Charlie. "But Oscar could be a silly boy, not sticking to the rules, taking unnecessary chances."

So that was his name. Oscar.

"How old was he?" I asked.

"I think he was a little bit older than you," said Michael. "But he wasn't sure of his exact age. He was an orphan, like you. And small. He'd been brought up in the East End by different families who treated him badly, so he ran away. He was living on the streets when we found him."

"He tried to pick Charlie's pocket," chuckled Emily.

Charlie nodded and gave a smile. "He was crude, but he had a raw talent for it," he said. "Michael caught him, and we offered him the chance of learning how to do it properly, just like we learned you."

"He was with us for six months," said Michael. "Then he got grabbed. Trouble was, the constable who took him in charge recognized him from before he was with us, when he was just living on the streets and thieving. It turns out Oscar had been arrested twice before. So when he came up in court this time, he got sentenced to seven years' transportation to Australia."

I let that thought sink in. Seven years' transportation. Plus six months in the middle of the ocean on the outward journey on a prison ship, with all the roughest and toughest criminals, and no place to run and hide if things got bad.

"So, you'd better make sure you don't get yourself grabbed," said Emily.

But I did. It was the very next week after we'd had that conversation in the coffee shop. We'd gone back to St Paul's Churchyard. It was the first time we'd been back since my first outing with the gang. But what we didn't know was that another gang had been at work there just the day before, so the shop owners were on the lookout for pickpockets. The last thing they wanted was for the Churchyard to get a bad reputation for ladies having their purses lifted. It would keep customers away.

We'd marked out our victim, a lady wearing an expensive-looking dress who'd come out of a pastry shop. There was no one with her, no friend or companion, so we thought we'd be safe. We did the usual, Charlie, Michael and Stephen giving me cover around her, while Emily stood nearby ready to take the purse from Charlie and slip it into her pocket. I was just closing my fingers around the cloth of the lady's purse when there was a shout of "Got you!"

I spun round, startled, and saw that Charlie had already moved into action, stepping in front of a man wearing an apron who'd obviously just come out from one of the shops.

"What's going on, my man?" demanded Charlie in his best upper-class voice, giving me time to run off, and I did … but a walking stick was thrust between my ankles and I tripped and fell to the pavement. The carrier of the

68

walking stick proceeded to hit me with it. I flung my arms up to protect myself, and started to protest, but it was no good. The man wearing the apron reached down and hauled me to my feet.

"Got you, you thief!" he shouted.

The woman I'd been dipping stood looking on, her face pale with shock.

"What's going on?" she asked.

The man with the apron stood me in front of her. "This thief had his hand in your pocket, ma'am!" he said. "We've had pickpockets operating here for the last two days, lifting purses from ladies like yourself, so we've been watching out for them." He shook me and gave me a smug and triumphant leer. "And now we've caught the thief!"

Chapter Twelve

Naturally, once they'd seen that I was properly caught, Charlie, Michael, Stephen and Emily had slipped away. This time I was taken to Blackfriars police station. That was lucky for me, because the desk sergeant and the other officers there had never seen me before. That meant that when I appeared before the magistrates at the court the next morning, they accepted my word that this was my first offence and that I'd never been in trouble with the law before.

I was sentenced to three months at Blackfriars Bridewell. I was full of fear, dreading that it would be just like Westminster Bridewell, and that it would be filled with the same sort of thugs and bullies who'd beaten me so badly there. But, to my pleasant surprise, I was put into a cell that wasn't too bad, and with a young boy of about my age who was also in for pickpocketing. The bunks were more comfortable than I'd had at Westminster, and that first evening I was given a bowl of hot soup and bread.

The reason for this came the next day. I was sitting on my bunk in my cell, talking to the other boy, whose name was Caleb, when the door of our cell opened and the turnkey looked in.

"Maybury," he said, "your sister's come to see you."

I was stunned. My sister! How could this be? I'd covered my tracks well since I'd arrived in London. There was no way my family could have tracked me down. And I had taken another surname to make sure my father didn't find me.

My mind was in a whirl as I followed the turnkey along the stone corridor, which was just as dark and damp-smelling as the corridor to the cells at Westminster. We went upstairs and then into a large plain room with benches placed about at tables. The turnkey handed me into the care of a waiting prison guard who took me to one of the benches. Emily was sitting there, and she got to her feet as I approached.

"Dick!" she smiled. "My poor brother!"

"Ten minutes," grunted the prison guard, and he went and stood against a wall at one side, watching us.

Emily grabbed my hand and pulled me down onto the bench beside her. "Don't worry, Dick. Charlie has taken care of things," she whispered.

I looked at her, puzzled.

"Care of things?" I repeated, bewildered. "What things?"

"Everything," she said. "You're in a nice cell, right? With someone friendly and safe?"

71

"Yes," I nodded.

"Good," said Emily. "Charlie's paid out good money to make sure you're treated right while you're in here. You'll get proper food, and the guards will take care of you. Make sure you don't come to any harm." She gave me a warm smile. "You're too valuable to us for anything bad to happen to you, Dick. Charlie told me to tell you that. We'll keep your place for you for when you come out. We've got someone to fill in for the moment, a cousin of Stephen's. He's all right, but he's not as good as you. But he'll do till you come out."

After that she chattered away about our non-existent family, our Ma and Pa, and how everyone was keeping and how they sent me their love and told me to be good while I sat and stared at her, my mind racing. Charlie had fixed things for me, she said. I could hardly take it in. I knew that you could bribe some of the constables because of the situation with Larry and the Adelphi gang, but I hadn't realized that someone could bribe the prison guards to make your life easier.

And then I remembered my time in Westminster, and how some of the prisoners had seemed to enjoy a much more pleasant time than others. They'd had good food, and were protected when they went out in the exercise yard. I'd thought they were special prisoners, but now I understood it was their money that got them those privileges. Or, at least, money paid by their friends.

"Tell Charlie, thank you," I whispered to Emily, as she got up to leave. "And, when I come out, he'll find he's got a friend for life."

"He'll be pleased to hear you say that," she smiled. "He'll see you when you come out. But I'll pop in every few weeks, just to make sure you're being treated well."

I have to say, I was treated well. Caleb was an amusing and pleasant companion as my cellmate. The guards kept a watchful eye on me when I strolled around the exercise yard during the times we were allowed out of our cell. And, for food, I was given meat, butter and pastries, in addition to the regular prison food. I shared my good food with Caleb, which made him even friendlier to me.

Everyone knew what I was in for, and most of them knew about the Flower and Dean Street gang, including Caleb.

"They've got a good reputation," he said to me one night, as we lay on our bunks in the cell. "I hear they're very sharp."

"Very sharp," I agreed with a nod, feeling proud that I was part of a well-known gang.

"And successful," added Caleb. "Judging by the way the warders treat you."

I winked at him and smiled.

"Very successful," I agreed. "They look after me as well

while I'm in here, as they do when we're outside."

"Pity you got caught," said Caleb. "I suppose they'll have replaced you by now."

I shook my head.

"Not me," I said. I flexed my fingers at him. "They need me and the things I can do with these fingers."

"Yeah, well, if you get out and find they have got someone else in your place, I know someone who'd be very glad of you."

"Oh?" I asked. "Who?" Not that I had any intention of moving to another gang, but I was always interested to find out about the opposition, people who were in the same line of business as we were, so to speak.

"He's a cousin of mine," he said. "His name's Monty. He runs a gang from Seven Dials. He's always on the lookout for a good tooler, especially little 'uns who look young, like you. He reckons that innocent little kid look is a winner, especially if trouble comes."

Seven Dials. I knew it well. It was a "rookery" just by Covent Garden. It was a slum, a maze of narrow streets where the police weren't happy about going because it was so rough. I used to walk through it sometimes when I was with the Adelphi gang.

I shook my head.

"Thanks for the offer, Caleb, but I think I'll stay with the people I know." I gestured at the remains of our supper, which were on the table. "Especially with the way they've looked after me while I'm in here."

When I came out of Blackfriars three months later, Emily was waiting at the prison gates for me.

"Ready to pick up again, Dick?" she asked.

I nodded. "I am," I told her, firmly.

Chapter Thirteen

It was good to be out of prison and back at Flower and Dean Street and to see the gang again. I didn't even have any complaints when Charlie told me I'd have to pay back some of the money he'd paid out in bribes to the guards at Blackfriars Bridewell. It was only fair, because he'd made sure my life in prison had been comfortable. Not just comfortable, at times it had been almost luxury with the hot food being served. True, the bunk I'd slept on had been hard and the mattress lumpy, but it had still been a lot more comfortable than the horsehair mattress in the tiny cramped room in Mrs Crust's lodging house, or the old prison van at the Adelphi.

After my capture and arrest at St Paul's Churchyard, we avoided that place and instead spent time further afield. We worked churches, theatres, open-air gatherings, and places where visitors packed in, like the waxworks at Madame Tussaud's. We also travelled out of town whenever there was a big occasion with loads of people guaranteed to be together in a crush. Places like Epsom Racecourse on Derby Day. Events like that, with so many thousands of people crowded together, made for easy pickings.

We also stuck to Charlie's rule about only going out once or twice a week.

In this way we carried on working the dip for three years. All the time I was growing up, and getting a bit taller. Not too tall, though. I was still small for my age. The one thing time brought me was practice. As the months, and then the years passed, I became even more nimble with my fingers.

I earned good money. I also spent it. Being with Charlie and the others, I'd acquired a taste for good clothes and fine food. I also had a room of my own in the house next to Charlie, Michael and Emily in Flower and Dean Street. Stephen had always lived separate from the others, a few streets away in Whitechapel. The room cost me money in rent, but I needed a place of my own, somewhere I could call home. I also wanted a place where I could keep my share of the loot, without anyone else having access to it. Charlie and Michael kept their share of the spoils in a bank, but I didn't trust banks. I preferred to have my money where I could see it and feel it, so I kept it locked in a strong metal box in a cupboard in my room with the key tied to a piece of string hung around my neck.

I suppose I knew that sooner or later my luck would run out again, but three years is a long time not to be caught, so I got a bit complacent.

This time we were in the Strand when we were spotted, again by a sharp-eyed shopkeeper, and I was grabbed and bundled into the shop and held while a police constable was called. He took me to Bow Street. Luckily for me there was no one at Bow Street who recognized me from my time with the Adelphi gang.

This time it was Charlie himself who came to see me in the custody cells. He'd bribed the duty sergeant to be allowed time to speak to me. He came straight to the point, his face serious.

"It ain't looking so good this time, Dick," he said. "I hear that old Wainthrop is the magistrate you'll be coming up before tomorrow. And you ain't a young boy no more. You're thirteen. In Wainthrop's eyes, that makes you a young man, responsible for his actions. And he's a hard man, keen on transportation."

Transportation! The word struck fear deep in my heart. I felt sick.

"What shall I do?" I asked, a feeling of panic rising inside me.

"This time you're going to need a lawyer," said Charlie. "But lawyers cost money."

"I've got money!" I said quickly.

Charlie nodded. "It's up to you, Dick," he said. "You can take a chance and plead for leniency, but my money says old Wainthrop ain't gonna go for that. Or you can

78

pay a lawyer to argue your case. He won't get you off, the evidence against you is too strong, but he might save you from transportation. It's up to you."

I didn't even think it over. I reached into my shirt and took the loop of string from round my neck with the key to my metal box, and handed it to Charlie.

"My money's in a box in my room," I told him. "There's the key to it. Hire a lawyer for me."

The lawyer Charlie got for me was a Mr Hackett, and he was good. Smooth-tongued, but not so slippery that the magistrate, old Wainthrop, despised him. Hackett had a good understanding of the law, too. He quoted different cases that had happened in the past, and how leniency had been given in this or that case. He talked about me being just a poor unfortunate orphan who'd been cruelly treated as a child and had run away to London to better himself, but had fallen on hard times. He also told the court this was my first offence. I don't know how he was able to cover up the fact I'd been arrested and imprisoned twice before, but he did.

I was found guilty but I was not going to be transported. Instead I was sentenced to six months at Westminster Bridewell. When I heard the words I felt sick to my stomach, remembering what had happened to me before when I was there. But then I cheered up, thinking how Charlie had made sure life was comfortable for me at Blackfriars, and I was sure he could do the same again for me now.

I was wrong. The prison had changed in the three years before. The buildings were the same, of course, but the prison guards were harder. And things seemed much stricter. I was marched to my cell and locked in. I was surprised to find there was only one bunk. And the turnkey who locked me in never uttered one word the whole time.

That night, the prison itself was silent, except for an occasional moan or cry. And those cries and moans were followed by a clatter of boots on stone, the banging of a heavy wooden baton on a metal door and a harsh guttural warning shout. The cries soon ceased.

The next morning I was taken from my cell and brought up before the prison governor. He was a large man with a bald head and dark brown bushy side-whiskers. He sat behind his large desk and surveyed me sternly as I stood in front of him.

"Stand up straight!" he barked.

I hadn't realized I was slouching. Because I didn't straighten up swiftly enough, the prison warder standing behind me poked me painfully in the small of the back with the end of his truncheon.

"Stand to attention!" the warder snapped.

I pulled myself up to my full height and stood to

attention, my hands straight down by my sides.

"The Silent System of punishment is in operation here, prisoner Maybury," the governor told me. "There is to be no talking to any other prisoners. You will not talk to any of the warders, or anyone else, unless you are ordered to. Do you understand?"

"Yes, sir."

"If you break that rule you will be punished. While you are here you will be exercised." Then he glared at me pointedly. "You will not want to come back." With that, he turned his attention to the warder accompanying me. "Take him away. Put him on the treadmill."

And so began six of the worst and most dreadful months of my life.

Chapter Fourteen

The Silent System was exactly that. Prisoners were forbidden to talk to one another, or make any noise at all. If they did they were put on hard punishments. I didn't think there could be any harder punishment than the treadmill, but I was to find out during my time there that I was wrong.

The treadmill was a huge wheel with long steps going right the way across. All the way along the steps, wooden boards had been fixed, so it was like a row of stalls, the sort you find with horse-boxes, only smaller. The prisoners were put into these stalls. Because of the boards you couldn't see the prisoner on either side of you, all you could see were the inside of the stalls and the step beneath your feet.

When the machine was started, the step beneath your feet went down, and you had to step up to the next one, like climbing a ladder, and then up to the next step, and so on. If you stopped then the step came down and hit your legs and threw you off. If that happened the warders would lift you up and beat you, and then put you back into the stall again. If you didn't want to be beaten, you walked, always uphill, at the speed set by the moving wheel and – for me – the wheel went fast.

If a prisoner refused to go on the treadmill, he could be flogged or birched as a punishment for this refusal and he'd be returned to the treadmill later. So we stayed, marching painfully ever upwards, and staying exactly where we were on the giant wheel.

Each group of prisoners walked on the treadmill for a quarter of an hour at a time. It doesn't sound much, but the constant tread upwards made the muscles of my legs and back ache. The sweat ran down my face and inside my clothes.

After what seemed like an eternity, but could only have been an hour or so, we were returned to our cells, and another group of prisoners took our places.

To make sure that no prisoners could break the Silent System and talk to one another, all the cells had been turned into small single cells, so that everyone was in solitary confinement.

Luckily we weren't put on the treadmill every day. Because there were so many prisoners at the Bridewell, we would do one day on, then one day off. On the days we weren't on the treadmill we were kept locked in our cells. On some days we were allowed out into the exercise yard, but again a strict rule of silence was observed. No one was allowed to talk. After three weeks of this, it became too much for me. One day, while I was walking around with the other prisoners I turned to the man nearest to me and burst out, "I can't stand this! I'm being driven mad!"

The man looked at me, shocked and horrified at my having spoken to him, and hastily turned away from me.

"I have to talk to someone!" I cried out.

That was as much as I was able to say, before two warders grabbed me and hustled me roughly back to my cell.

A short time later I found myself standing once more before the prisoner governor. He looked at me, unfeelingly.

"You have broken the first rule of Silent Punishment," he said. "You will be given twelve strokes of the birch." He turned his attention to the warders with me. This time there were two of them present, in case I attempted to do anything foolish, like attack the governor. "Then put him on shot drill for two days." Turning back to me, he said, "I think that will make you appreciate the wisdom of keeping to the rules while you are here."

I was marched out of the governor's office and taken to the punishment room. There, my shirt was stripped off me, and my wrists were manacled just above my head to a large heavy wooden frame.

One of the warders went to a cupboard and took out a long cane made of birch. I knew what was coming and tensed myself, ready for the first blow. Even though I was ready for it, it hurt deeply as the first stroke of the birch slashed across my bare back. A pause, then the second stroke hit me. I bit my lip to try and stop myself crying out, but the third stroke – on top of the place where the first two had landed – filled me with so much pain that I couldn't help but cry out. As the cane landed for the fourth time I felt wetness on my back, and knew it had cut into my skin and drawn blood. The rest of the punishment was just a haze of pain, and I gritted my teeth and just prayed it would end soon. When it did, after the twelfth cut of the cane, the warders unshackled me from the frame. I felt them step away from me after they did so, expecting me to fall to the floor, but I was determined not to give them that satisfaction.

One of them thrust my shirt into my arms, and then they marched me back to my cell. Once there, after the door had clanged shut on me, I lay face down on my hard bench, stuffed my face into my crumpled-up shirt, and sobbed silently, biting my lip to stop my cries coming out and being heard.

I was in Hell.

The next day I discovered what sort of punishment shot drill was. The treadmill was hard, but shot drill was so much harder.

Those prisoners who were on shot drill were marched

into the exercise yard. Only the warders were there, no other prisoners. Heavy black cannon balls had been laid out in a large square, about three yards apart. We stood one prisoner by each cannon ball. One of the warders took his position in the centre of the square and studied us all. Then he shouted, "Lift!"

I saw the other prisoners reach down and pick up the cannon ball. I did the same. It was very heavy, especially for someone like me, who was small.

"Left!" shouted the warder.

I and the other prisoners then stumbled three yards to our left, to the same place where another prisoner had been standing just before.

"Stop!" shouted the warder.

We stopped.

"Down!" shouted the warder.

We put the cannon balls down on the ground, then stood up straight again.

"Right!"

This time we walked to our right, back to our original position, where another heavy cannon ball was now lying.

"Change!" shouted the warder.

We put down the ball we were carrying, then lifted the other ball, and then went through the whole back-breaking routine again. And all the time staying silent. The only sounds were the shouted commands from the warder in the centre of the square, and the painful breathing of the prisoners as we hauled the heavy cannon balls.

I wasn't sure how long the drill went on for. After a while my body became numb, my legs and arms aching, and all I could feel was pain.

Finally, as we dropped the cannon ball for the umpteenth time, came the command: "Stop!" And then we were marched back to our cells. Once back in my cell, I collapsed onto my bench and felt every part of me burn with agony.

Never again, I vowed to myself. Never again.

Chapter Fifteen

This time, when I came out of the prison gates, there was no one to meet me. No Charlie, no Emily, no Michael or even Stephen. I made my way to Flower and Dean Street, wondering if the gang would still be there. It had been six months since I'd last seen any of them. During my time in Westminster Bridewell I'd had no word from them, no visits, not even a note. For all I knew they might have been arrested themselves and been sent to prison.

I went to the house where I'd had my room before I'd gone to prison, but the landlady told me there was someone else living there now. In a way, I should have expected it. A room in London doesn't stay empty for long but part of me had hoped that Charlie and the others would keep paying the rent on it to keep it ready for me when I came out.

Instead, I went to the house where Charlie, Emily and Michael had their rooms. The landlady was out, and a girl I'd never seen before was inside, cleaning. I asked her if I could wait in the sitting room for my friends to come back, but she looked at me suspiciously and told me her mistress had given strict orders not to allow strangers in. So I was forced to wait outside in the street, hanging around and getting more and more miserable as I waited for the gang to return.

It was later afternoon when I saw Charlie and Emily coming down the street accompanied by a small boy.

"Dick!" called Charlie cheerfully when he saw me. He hurried forward and held out his hand, and we shook. "Was it today you came out?"

"Yes," I grunted, still hurt that there'd been no one to meet me.

Charlie sighed, gave an apologetic smile and shook his head. "I could have sworn it was tomorrow," he said. "But then, things have been hard of late. Lots of things to think about. Michael and Stephen leaving."

"Leaving?"

Charlie nodded. "They set up on their own," he said. He gestured towards the small boy, who was looking at me with a wary look on his face. "This is Matthew," he said.

My replacement, I thought. I nodded at him in greeting, and he nodded back, but he didn't smile, just looked at me suspiciously. He was probably wondering whether or not he still had a job now I was back.

"What was it like inside?" asked Emily, her voice concerned.

"It was dreadful," I said. "The worst time I've ever known." Briefly, I told them about the Silent System, the treadmill, the shot drill, and being birched. Emily shuddered as I told my story, and Charlie looked unhappy.

"That's why we couldn't come and see you," he said, apologetically. "Or make life easier for you, like we did when you were in Blackfriars. It's the new rules."

"Did they really birch you?" asked Matthew, speaking for the first time.

I nodded.

"Just once," I answered. "But it was enough." I gestured towards the house I used to live in. "My room's gone," I said.

Charlie sighed again. "We had to let it go, Dick. For a while, there were slim pickings, especially after Michael and Stephen left. We had to train young Matthew here, and then a couple of new stalls, and all that time there was no money coming in."

"I had money!" I said. "It was in my box. There was enough to pay the rent on my room."

Charlie looked uncomfortable. "Why don't we go inside," he said, motioning towards the house where he and Emily had their rooms. "We don't want to have this sort of conversation out in the street where everyone can hear." He turned to Matthew and gave him a shilling. "Run along and get yourself something, Matthew. We'll see you later. Emily and I need to have a talk with Dick."

Matthew took the coin, gave me a last wary look,

and then hurried off. Once inside their rooms, we sat ourselves down. It had been six months since I'd sat in a comfortable chair, and it felt strange after the hard benches of Westminster Bridewell.

"The fact is, your lawyer cost a lot of money," said Charlie. "You were up for transportation for sure. So, with his fees, and his clerk's, and the money to the clerk of the court..."

"How much do I have left?" I asked, giving him a hard stare.

"Five pounds," said Charlie.

"Five pounds?" I echoed, stunned. There had been fifty pounds in my box when I'd been arrested. I knew because I'd just counted it.

"Like I said, the lawyer cost a lot of money..." said Charlie defensively.

"Forty-five pounds!" I challenged him.

Charlie looked back at me, hurt.

"If you're suggesting that we took your money..." he said, angry.

I glared back at him. "All I'm saying is that forty-five pounds seems a lot of money to pay for a lawyer for just one session in court. Especially as I was found guilty."

"Charlie did his best for you, Dick," cut in Emily. "It wasn't just the lawyer to pay. There was the police, so your previous convictions didn't come up in court."

Charlie nodded. "If it had come out this was your third conviction, you'd have been transported for sure. The lawyer had to make sure the right people were squared, so that stuff didn't come up."

"Five pounds?" I said again, my voice sounding hollow and dull even to me.

Charlie and Emily nodded, their faces unhappy.

"We'd give you more if we could, Dick," said Charlie. "But with Michael and Stephen gone …"

"And this new boy ain't as good as you," said Emily, smiling for the first time. "I was saying to Charlie only yesterday, once Dick gets out we'll be able to get back in the swing again. Back in the money!"

"But of course, we've got to be fair by Matthew," added Charlie, quickly. "We can't just put him off like that."

"So what happens to me?" I demanded.

"Give it a couple of weeks," said Charlie. He brightened up. "Maybe you and Matthew could share the work," he suggested. "One day he could come out with us, then the next you do."

"That's good," nodded Emily. "Less chance of people getting suspicious when they see you."

"So I take less money," I grunted.

"Well, fair's fair, Dick," said Charlie. "We can't pay you for Matthew's work, can we? It's the tooler that earns the money."

"Exactly!" I snapped back at him. "Neither of you would have those fine clothes, or these rooms, if it hadn't been for me and my fingers!"

"Now hold on, Dick," said Charlie sharply. "You wouldn't have had those clever fingers of yours if we hadn't trained you up. Remember, when me and Michael picked you up, you'd just come out of Westminster Bridewell for stealing gentlemen's handkerchiefs. If it hadn't been for us, you'd still be with the Adelphi gang. If they'd have you."

My eyes told them how angry I was. Angry at having lost six months of my life to the hard labour and cruel conditions in Westminster, and the feeling that these people who I thought were my friends had betrayed me and stolen my money. Yes, it was true that my lawyer had cost money, but a nagging doubt in my mind told me it hadn't been as much as forty-five pounds. I held out my hand. "I think I'd better take my money and go," I said.

Emily looked uncomfortable. Charlie returned my stare. "Is this the end of the road for us, then, Dick?" he asked. "I need to know, on account of what to tell Matthew."

I hesitated, then nodded. "I reckon it is," I said.

Charlie's face tightened. Then he went to a cupboard, opened it up, took out my metal money box, and offered it to me, along with the key.

"I don't need the box," I told him sharply. "I can't carry it around the streets with me."

"Very well," he said, still looking angrily at me.

I unlocked the box and took out the money that was in there. It was all in coins, which was useful because questions might be asked if I started producing bank notes. I put the money in my jacket pocket.

"Goodbye," I said, my voice flat, offering them no warmth.

I thought that Emily looked as if she was about to burst into tears, but she didn't. "Goodbye, Dick," nodded Charlie.

With that, I left their rooms and went downstairs and out into the street. I was thirteen years old, and alone again.

Chapter Sixteen

I was still feeling angry when I left Charlie and Emily's house, angry at them for treating me the way they did, and angry at myself for letting myself be cheated. I couldn't prove they had cheated me, but it felt to me as if they had, and that was enough. But as I walked along Flower and Dean Street, I felt sad as well. We'd been together as a gang for three years. It felt like I was leaving a big part of my life behind me, a part that had been good, for the money, and for the friendship. Now that friendship, and my money, were gone.

I decided I couldn't stay in the Whitechapel area. I didn't want to see Charlie or Emily again. I knew I couldn't go back to the Adelphi and the gang there. I'd outgrown them, and anyway, Larry wouldn't want me back in the gang, not now I'd been to prison. But it was that part of London where the richest pickings were to be had, around the Strand.

It was strange. All the time I was in prison I had vowed that I wouldn't ever go back in there again. Never ever. Yet here I was, just out, and already thinking about picking

95

pockets again. It was stupid. It had been thieving that had put me in prison, not just once but three times, and the last time for the worst and harshest experience ever. And the chances were that next time it wouldn't be prison, but transportation.

But what lawful work could I do that would give me as good a life as I'd had when I was with Charlie and Emily and the Flower and Dean Street gang? I was poor. I had no proper education beyond elementary school, and lessons from my mother. The only choices open to me were hard labour for pennies, working in a slaughterhouse like Daniel, or a crossing sweeper spending every day barefoot in horse dung, or a mudlark, or other hard and dirty occupations. That life wasn't for me. I wanted better.

Then I remembered what Caleb had told me when I was in Blackfriars, about his cousin Monty in Seven Dials. And Seven Dials was next to Covent Garden and close by the Strand, and a good distance from Whitechapel.

The area was called Seven Dials because seven streets met together in a square. I'd been told that once, many years ago, there had been a tall stone column in the middle of this square, with a sundial on each side, which was how the place got its name, but this column had been taken down long ago. Whatever the reason for its name, this was the place I headed to. With only five pounds in my pocket, and not confident about when I'd next be able to lay my hands on any money, I had to find lodgings that were cheap.

I found a room in a house in Earlham Street. In a slum like Seven Dials I could afford to rent a whole room to myself and not have to share, which would have been the case in a more expensive part of town. Of course, anyone wearing the smart clothes that I was dressed in, in a place like Seven Dials, stood out as being some kind of crook. No real gentleman would live in a place like Seven Dials, not if he cared for his social position.

The day I moved into Seven Dials was also my fourteenth birthday. Not that there was much cause for celebration, except for the fact that I was out of that nightmarish prison.

It didn't take me long to find Monty, especially once I used Caleb's name. In fact there were lots of different gangs living in the area, which was also known as the St Giles rookery. These vast areas of slums were known as rookeries because they were similar to the rooks' nests found in trees, where huge numbers of rooks gathered together, so many they couldn't be counted, and always ready to fly off at the first sign of trouble. That was the way it was in the slum rookeries of London. The numbers of people living in them were so vast, and the streets were such a maze, that the police preferred not to go into them, unless they were forced to. This made them safe places to stay for people like me, who earned their living by crime.

By the end of that first day I'd tracked Monty down to

a coffee house near the central crossing. He was a tall, thin man, with a lock of hair that went across his otherwise bald head and seemed to be stuck down with wax. But his clothes were smart and clean, if a bit old and worn.

"So you're the boy from the famous Flower and Dean Street gang," he said with a smile. But it wasn't a real smile, not the sort of welcoming smiles that Charlie and Michael had given me when I first met them. It was a smile in his mouth only. Monty's eyes were cold and hard, and always looking past me, or anyone else he was talking to. "Caleb told me about you. He said you were good."

"I am," I said.

I waited for him to ask why I'd left the Flower and Dean Street gang, but he didn't. Instead, he said, "As it happens, we have an opening just now for someone in your line of work."

"Oh?" I asked.

"Yes," he said. "Our boy unfortunately got himself caught."

"It happens," I said with a shrug. "Bad luck strikes everyone."

Monty shook his head. "He was careless," he said. Then, examining me with his head slightly to one side, and looking a bit like a vulture you see in a zoo, he enquired softly, "I hope you haven't become careless?"

For a second I was deeply offended. I'd come from one of

the best gangs in London, and here was this man with stuck-down hair and wearing a shabby suit in one of the city's worst slums asking me if I was any good. I nearly told him to forget it there and then, but I reflected that I needed to get in with a gang quickly to start earning some money. Once I'd got a few pounds in my pocket again, I could walk away from Monty and look for something better.

"No," I told him firmly. "I haven't become careless. I'm the best there is!"

Monty studied me, then nodded. "Very well," he said. "We'll see how it works out."

And that's how I joined the Seven Dials gang.

Because they'd recently had their tooler arrested in the Strand, and the rest of the gang were worried they might be recognized if they operated in that same area so soon after that, they had decided to operate on new ground, in particular avoiding expensive shops, which is where their tooler had been caught. So we worked the Zoo at Regent's Park, then the crowds outside Madame Tussaud's Waxworks, and theatregoers leaving a performance.

It was while I was with Monty and the Seven Dials gang that I met Sally. She was fifteen and a maltooler, which meant a pickpocket who stole from people travelling on omnibuses.

Like me, she said she was an orphan, but I suspected that she was really a runaway like I was. She never mentioned her family at all. It didn't matter. That was the thing about living in a big city like London, you could give yourself a new name and a new everything, and that's who you were, providing you could carry it off.

The thing is, with Sally, I liked her straight away, as soon as I met her. She was the one person I'd met who didn't seem to want me only for what money she could make out of me. She was pretty, and she made me laugh. We hung around with the crowd at Seven Dials, and then gradually we found we were going around the town together, just us two. She was my first sweetheart, but I felt she was the right one for me. I knew she didn't like where she lived because a lot of the other people in her house were drunks and you never know when they're going to come bursting into your room, or start fighting outside your door. One evening she was telling me about the troubles in her house, and how she sometimes wondered if she was going to get killed in her bed, so I asked her to move in with me. "I'll look after you and keep you safe," I promised.

When I said that, her face lit up, and she gave me a big kiss. "I was hoping you'd say that," she said with a smile.

So that was how Sally moved in with me and we became a couple.

I was a lot happier living with Sally but there was one thing I'd noticed recently that worried me – every now and then, my fingers trembled when I went to lift a purse or pick a pocket. I was certain it was the result of the horrible experience I'd suffered in Westminster Bridewell. I didn't know whether the treadmill or the shot drill had drained me and affected my health or whether it was the fear of being locked up again. Fortunately, it didn't happen very often, and when it did I told Monty and the rest of the stalls that the pocket was too tight and so too dangerous, that there was a chance we could get caught. Luckily for me, the trembling soon passed, and I'd then move on to another lady and dip her pocket successfully, so that kept the gang happy. Otherwise I knew they'd kick me out.

I tried to get it under control. When I got back to the room that Sally and I shared, I practised dipping and lifting. Sally came back from work one day to find me holding my right hand with my left, pressing my fingers tightly together, and asked what I was up to. I told her it was just cramp, and then we went out for the evening together and celebrated her good day's work on the omnibuses. But, at the back of my mind, there was a fear that one day my hand would lead me back inside the Bridewell, on the treadmill and locked in brutal silence.

Chapter Seventeen

It's often struck me as strange that you can live in a place like London, right near to people you know, and never see them from one year's end to the other. It struck me now as I was working with the Seven Dials gang and our paths took us into the Strand, and I looked across the road and thought of the Adelphi gang, tucked away in the old prison van.

I promised myself that one evening I'd take a stroll down to the van just to catch up with the gang for old times' sake, but it never happened. There was always something to do. And also, by this time, I was very happy spending my time with Sally, and I didn't think she'd fancy coming along with me and spending an evening with a bunch of pickpockets who lived in a van.

It was just over two years this time before I was caught again. During that time, Sally and I moved to bigger and better rooms in a nicer house in Seven Dials. We had thought of moving a bit further away, but the fact was that we were with our own kind in Seven Dials, and that made us feel safe.

At the time I got caught, our gang was working Regent's Park, and unfortunately my fingers started to tremble just as I'd taken hold of the purse in a lady's skirt pocket. Even with her thick petticoats, her stays and corsets, she must have felt her skirt shake, because she turned and saw me. Her mouth opened and she gave a cry of "Oh! Thief!" In desperation I turned to run, but a blow from a gentleman's walking stick caught me on the shin. I fell to the ground, and was soon grabbed.

When the constable arrived I blustered and tried to say that I was just catching a butterfly that had landed on the woman's skirt. Even as I said it, I knew it sounded a feeble excuse, but I had little choice. Usually I would have denied the charge and accused the lady of being mistaken, or said it had been someone else, but as she had seen me with my hand actually inside her pocket, I really had no proper defence, as I knew the court would believe the lady's story rather than mine.

When I appeared in court I couldn't afford a lawyer, so I tried my excuse. The problem was, I had no one to stand up in court and give me a character reference. There was no employer, no family member, all of which looked bad for me.

Luckily, possibly because I was charged at a police station that was new to me, and tried at a magistrate's court where the magistrate had never seen me before, my past crimes weren't brought up. My guess was that no one had bothered to check up and see if I had any previous convictions.

I was sentenced to ten months in prison, this time at Coldbath Fields in Clerkenwell. I soon discovered that the regime at Coldbath Fields was somewhere between the harsh system at Westminster and the lighter one at Blackfriars. It was a prison mainly for women and children, with some men, and most prisoners were only there serving short sentences.

Even though Coldbath Fields had a reputation as a "hard" prison, the Silent System of punishment that had been brought in at Westminster hadn't yet been introduced there.

One good thing was, I still had some money on me. It was not enough to pay for a lawyer, but enough to pay the prison warders to ensure that I had some luxuries: tea to drink, and decent food to eat.

During my time in prison, Sally came to visit me every week, bringing treats and nice foods for me when she could. I was touched by the fact that she always came, whatever the weather, and no matter how busy she was. Sometimes, when she came to visit me, she looked really tired. I said to her once, when she was looking really worn down, "You don't always have to come and visit, Sally. I don't want you wearing yourself out and taking ill. I'll be out soon, and we'll be able to see each other every day."

Sally gave me a small smile and shook her head.

"I ain't gonna let you forget me as easy as that, Dick," she said. "I said I'd come and see you every week, and I will. You and me, we're a pair. Don't you forget it."

And I didn't. Every day I was in Coldbath Fields I thought of Sally and swore to myself that when I came out I'd make it up to her and give her a good life.

I'd been in Coldbath for six months when one day I was in the prison courtyard, taking my exercise walk and to my surprise, I saw Finlay from the Adelphi gang sitting on the ground by one of the high walls.

"Finlay!" I said.

He looked up, and he almost smiled. Almost, but not quite. He looked miserable.

"Dick," he said, getting to his feet. He looked around at the prison buildings and sighed heavily. "Just our luck to meet up again in a place like this."

"It could be worse," I said. "Westminster wasn't as easy the first time as Patrick's sister said it was going to be and the second time it was a nightmare experience."

"The Silent System?" he asked.

I nodded. "At least in this place you can talk to others." I looked at him, at the unhappy manner of him. "So, you got caught," I said.

"Yes," he said gloomily. He sighed again. "We got sloppy. If you ask me, the old gang went to pot after Joe died."

I stared at him, stunned.

"Joe's dead?"

"Didn't you hear about it?" he asked. "It happened four months ago."

"I've been in here for the last six," I said. "How did it happen?"

"Patrick got caught down at the station dipping for a handkerchief. Joe stepped in and tried to help him escape but the man Patrick was dipping hit out with his cane and he caught Joe. Joe went down and hit his head on the cobbles." Finlay sighed. "That was it."

I looked at him, shocked.

"Just hitting his head on the ground?" I said, stunned.

Finlay nodded.

"The swell who hit Joe turned out to be a magistrate, so the police said there'd be no charges against him. They said it was an accident."

"So, who's in charge of the gang now?" I asked.

"Abel took over, but he can't think like Joe," said Finlay. "He waits for Larry to come and tell him what to do." He sighed again. "Like I say, it ain't the same. I got caught two days ago."

"How long did you get?" I asked.

"Six months," Finlay replied. He gave another heavy sigh. "I don't think I'll be going back to the gang when I come out."

That night as I lay on my bunk in my cell I thought of Joe, who'd been so friendly to me when I first met up with the Adelphi gang, and had made sure he taught me properly so I wouldn't get caught easily. The fact I did get caught hadn't been Joe's fault. Joe had been honest and fair in the way he'd made sure that everyone got their proper payment for the handkerchiefs they took, and no one got cheated. Yes, he was a thief, but he was a decent person. If the world had been different and he'd come from a different class, or a different family, he'd likely have been a successful businessman. But instead, he was dead, clubbed down by someone who'd got away with it because he was a magistrate. Life wasn't fair.

I didn't see a great deal of Finlay during the rest of my time at Coldbath. The times we were let out for exercise in the yard varied. When we were both in the yard at the same time, Finlay looked so miserable that I didn't really want to get into a conversation with him, because he'd only make me feel worse about my situation.

The week before I was due to get out of the prison, I did make a point of seeking Finlay out to wish him well and ask him to pass on my good wishes to the other boys if he saw them. But he just looked at me in a sour way.

"Didn't you hear what I said, Dick?" he scowled. "I'm not going back to them."

Then he dropped his eyes from me and slumped down

on the ground, with his back against the wall. I noticed that he'd let himself go since I'd last seen him in the yard: his hair was long and dirty and he smelt. I guessed he hadn't washed himself in a long time. I thought to myself that the Adelphi gang wouldn't want him back in that condition, the smell of him would draw unwanted attention to him from the boat customers.

I stood looking down at him, his head slumped forward, looking so miserable and fragile.

"In that case, I wish you well when you get out," I said. And I left him, sitting there on the ground. He didn't answer me, or even look up.

By the time I came out of Coldbath Fields after my ten-month sentence, I realized I'd been earning my living as a pickpocket in London for eight years, ever since I was nine years old, and I'd been in prison four times. So far I'd been lucky, I'd avoided a very long jail sentence, and I'd also escaped transportation. If I'd been clever, my last prison sentence would have been a warning not to keep taking chances, and I would have left London with Sally and tried to make a fresh start. After all, I was now seventeen years old and an adult, something that would open new opportunities for work that was legal. But Sally wasn't ready to leave London. It was the only place she'd known. It was her home, and she wanted to stay. And I wanted us both to have the good things in life. So, instead, I returned to crime.

As soon as I came out of prison I went back to the house in Seven Dials, where Sally had kept our rooms. My old crowd had got themselves a new tooler while I'd been inside, but I soon linked up with another mob that operated out of Seven Dials.

There were four of them in the gang: Edward, Peter, Sean and his sweetheart, Mary. Edward was the leader. He was about thirty, very tall and thin, and – as with Charlie and Michael – always very well dressed. He had longish dark hair that curled over his high collar, and a way of looking down his nose at you that told you he felt he was superior. His real affectation was wearing a fresh flower in the buttonhole of his jacket whenever we went out on a job. He said it was his lucky talisman; he was sure that no policeman would arrest someone with a real flower in his buttonhole because that person was so obviously a gentleman. Personally, I doubted it, but Edward said he'd never ever been pinched, so it worked for him.

Peter was the opposite of Edward in almost every way. Peter was quite short and also tubby. Although he also dressed in good clothes, they always seemed to be a size too small. It was as if he was just about to burst out of them. Whereas Edward had a luxuriant head of hair, Peter was nearly bald, even though he was only just about thirty.

And Peter's shoes always looked a bit worse for wear, while Edward's shone from where he polished them at least twice a day.

Sean and Mary, like me, were new members of the gang, replacing another couple who'd decided to leave London and move to Bristol. They'd been with Edward and Peter for about a month before I joined. Sean and Mary reminded me of a couple of foxes. They both had that shifty look, eyes looking every which way, and their manner always seemed as if they were ready to pounce on an unwilling victim. Interestingly enough they both had red hair, and at first I thought they must be related, but it turned out that Sean's parents were originally from Cork in Ireland, and Mary's from Glasgow, with no family connection between them.

The gang didn't specialize in taking ladies' purses, as the Flower and Dean Street gang had done, they targeted everyone and everything. They worked wherever there was a big gathering of people. The bigger the better: racecourses, theatres, the zoo, big political rallies. If there was going to be a large crowd anywhere, this gang would be there, too, dipping and lifting. I'd been working with them for just a few weeks when they told me there was going to be one of the biggest meetings of people held in London for many years. It was a Chartists' Rally, to be held at Kennington Common, just across the River Thames in south London. Hundreds of thousands of people were expected to attend.

"And hundreds of thousands of people means hundreds of thousands of pockets and purses and wallets," grinned Edward. "It'll be rich pickings!"

I had heard a bit about the Chartists back when I was at home in Shropshire, because my father had railed against them as ungodly. At the time I didn't understand what he was going on about and I assumed they were just another religious organization; there seemed to be so many springing up, all of which my father disapproved of. But this time I decided to find out more about them before we went off to Kennington Common. It helps to know what sort of people will be at a place, to help you choose your victims. It's no use picking the pocket of a poor person. So, at racecourses, we'd wait until we watched someone collect their winnings from one of the bookmakers, or someone collect their change from one of the food vendors, and assess the size of their wallet.

At first, when I read about these Chartists, they didn't seem to offer much in the way of rich pickings. It all seemed to be about getting fair representation in Parliament, especially for poor and ordinary people. I said as much to Edward, but he shook his head.

"No, Dick," he said. "There are just as many wealthy people as poor amongst these Chartists. More, in fact.

Most poor people don't have the time or the money to go to meetings like this. Trust me, it will be the easiest job you've ever done!"

Chapter Eighteen

We got to Kennington Common late in the morning of Monday 10th April, and already there were thousands of people gathered there, milling around, most of them near a platform that had been set up on the Common. As we reached the place, more and more people were arriving, many of them marching together in long lines, some with banners and placards. There were placards from all over London: Stepney Green, Peckham and many other boroughs. It was the largest gathering of people I had ever seen. There was also a huge number of police in attendance, thousands and thousands. Worried, I pointed this out to Edward.

"It's going to be hard pulling any tricks with that many police around," I said.

Edward shook his head. "They won't be watching out for the likes of us," he said confidently. "They're here to make sure it doesn't turn into a riot. They're worried all this lot are going to march on Parliament."

"Why would they do that?" I asked.

"To present the petition," said Peter. He grinned. "Don't you ever read the papers, Dick?"

The truth was, I didn't. At least, not about politics because it bored me.

Peter pointed to the platform that had been set up. "That's where the leader of this lot, a man called Feargus O'Connor, is going to address the crowd," he said. "According to the papers, they've got over a million people to sign a petition calling for Parliament to bring in new rules to make things fairer when electing Members of Parliament. O'Connor is going to carry the petition to Parliament from here. But he's been told he can only take so many of his people with him to bring the petition. If more than the number allowed try to go along, the government have said it will be considered a riot, and the military will move in and stop them."

"By shooting them," added Edward. "There are soldiers at the bridges across the Thames. If a mob tries to cross, they'll open fire."

I looked around the edges of the Common, at the rows of policemen, and saw that – sure enough – there were uniformed soldiers in the background, and they had rifles. A shiver of fear went through me. All it needed was for some hothead to start shouting and stir this lot up and the soldiers would open fire on everyone. We could all die.

"This is a dangerous place to be," I muttered. "We could all be shot."

"Not if we stay near the platform where the speaker is,"

said Peter confidently. "The soldiers will stay at the edge of the crowd, so the ones who'll get shot will be those at the north side of the Common."

I still wasn't reassured, but what Peter and Edward said made sense, so I made my way with them, pushing through the crowd towards the platform. Sean and Mary were already there, eating sausages they'd bought from one of the food vendors.

"Isn't this exciting!" said Mary. "Such a crowd!" She lowered her voice to a whisper and winked at me as she murmured, "There should be good pickings today!"

"Best wait till the speeches start," suggested Edward. "Then all the attention will be on the speakers on the platform."

"Nearer the back of the crowd will be best," said Mary. "That's where the ladies will be. They won't want to get crushed."

"Good thinking," nodded Peter, and we moved back towards the fringes of the crowd packed around the platform, still waiting for the speakers to step up and address the crowd. Posts had been hammered into the ground carrying placards with different slogans. I saw one that said: "To the Working Men of London. The grievances of the Working Class are just. We and our families are pining in misery and starvation. We demand a fair day's wage for a fair day's work. We are the slaves of capital – we demand protection for our labour. We are political serfs – we demand to be free. It is for the Good of All that we seek to restore the evils under which we groan."

I pointed this out to Edward.

"That doesn't sound like someone with lots of money," I commented.

"That's just one placard," shrugged Edward. "For every poor person there will be those with money in their purse. This isn't just a political rally, Dick, it's a grand day out!"

Suddenly I heard a cheery voice call out: "Dick!"

I spun round, and saw John Jarvey, smiling broadly, arm in arm with a young woman.

"I thought that was you!" said John, and he came striding happily towards me.

"I'll see you in a minute," I whispered to Edward and the others.

The gang nodded and drifted away, but only to where they could still see me, while pretending to be part of the crowd.

"Dick, I'd like you to meet Peg," said John.

The young woman by his side smiled at me. She was dressed up in a flowery gown, with a bonnet trimmed with lace. Her clothes weren't too fancy and expensive, but they were smart and clean.

"Hello," she said.

"This is my old pal, Dick Maybury," said John. He gave

me a broad and admiring smile. "Me and him roomed together when he first came to London."

"That's right," I said. "Though it seems a long time ago."

John looked at the way I was dressed, my expensive clothes and hat, admiringly.

"You're still looking very dapper, Dick."

I certainly cut a smarter figure than John did. Like his sweetheart, Peg, his clothes were neat and clean but old, and here and there I could see the signs of mending. I smiled at him and nodded back.

"It goes with the business, John," I admitted.

"What business are you in, Mr Maybury?" asked Peg.

"Finance," I said. Then, to change the subject quickly before she could ask any more questions, I turned to John and asked, "So, what are you doing here, John?"

"We thought it would be a good day out. Didn't we, Peg?"

"Yes indeed," nodded Peg. "John wanted to come for the politics and the speeches, but I just wanted to see the crowds." She looked around at the mass of people gathered there, thousands of them, with a look of awe. "I've never seen so many people in one place!"

"You interested in politics then, John?" I asked.

"It's the way forward if people like us are going to get a fair share," said John. "All people are created equal.

117

The Chartists will give us a chance to do things properly so that we all get a fair chance in this life."

Peg gave a little laugh.

"He's been saying that for ages," she said. "I told him he should stand for Parliament."

"That's the point, no one can unless they've got money and position," said John, his voice earnest now. "People like us will never get a decent chance unless there are changes in the way Parliament is run."

"But we have got a decent chance," countered Peg. She turned to me and said proudly, "John's manager of his shop now, and there's a good chance of getting a shop of our very own." She turned back to John and said, "And you've done all that without any politicians helping you, or any changes in the law. You've done it because you've worked hard and shown you're honest."

"Yes, but –" began John.

"No buts," said Peg firmly. "You've worked for what you've got." Turning back to me, she said, "It may not seem a lot, but from where John's come from, he's made great strides. And when we get the ironmonger's –"

"An ironmonger's?" I echoed, surprised.

John nodded.

"We're going to rent a shop and start an ironmonger's," he said. "It's the coming business."

"There's a big demand for ironmongery, with all the

building works that's going on," said Peg enthusiastically. And then she leaned in to John, gave his arm an affectionate squeeze and kissed him on the cheek. "Which means me and John will have enough to get married and get a little house of our own."

"Married!" I exulted, and I stepped forward and took first John's hand, and then Peg's, and shook them warmly. "Congratulations! That's wonderful!"

Just then Edward appeared beside us.

"Excuse my interrupting," he smiled at John and Peg, "but we need to take Dick away from you. I promised Dick I'd introduce him to my uncle, and the old chap says he's not feeling well and has got to leave."

"Oh, that's sad," said Peg, looking concerned. "What's wrong with him?"

"Gout," said Edward. "He can't stand for long." Turning back to me, he said, "I'm sorry to cut in on you and your friends like this, Dick—"

"No, no," I assured him. "I'm sure that John and Peg understand."

"Of course we do!" said Peg. "My Grandad had gout. It's a real terror! You go off and see your friend's uncle."

"I'm sure we'll catch up with you later, Dick," beamed John.

I gave John and Peg a broad smile, and then I walked off with Edward and rejoined the others.

"We'd better make sure we stay away from them," murmured Edward. "We don't want them watching you while we're doing the business."

"Don't worry," I assured him. "I'll make sure we stay well clear of them."

In fact, we made sure that we kept on the move the whole afternoon, not just to keep away from John and Peg, but to avoid anyone else who might be keeping too close an eye on us. As soon as I'd lifted one purse from a lady's skirt pocket, we separated – to avoid being spotted as a gang – and then moved to the other side of the Common before pulling the trick a second time. We made sure that, although we were on the fringes of the crowd, we were far enough in to be away from the gaze of the watching police, and for the crush of the assembled throng to give us safe cover.

By early afternoon we'd taken three purses and gained just over four pounds, which was a reasonable haul. I'd also avoided running into John and Peg again, which wasn't too difficult because of the huge size of the crowd. However, I couldn't get the thought of them out of my mind. So John was now a shop manager, and he and Peg were going to get married and run their own ironmonger's shop, and find themselves a little house of their own. It was true what Peg had said, he'd come a long way since I'd first met him, in that tiny, stuffy attic room in Mrs Crust's house. There was a side of me that envied him. He didn't look as well off as me: his clothes were older and more worn than mine and Peg's dress looked like it had been mended a few times, but they seemed happy together. No, more than happy, they seemed settled. Comfortable. And they had a future planned out. Something to aim for. That was one thing that couldn't be said about the life that Sally and I were living.

One day we'd be rich, spending pound notes as if they were farthings. Then, a few days later, we'd be struggling to find a few coins to pay for food. We never seemed to be able to hang on to the money; there were always people to pay. I suppose it was our own fault. When we had money we tended to live the high life, going to the theatre and entertainment places like the Coal Hole, buying good food and good wine. It was fun, but then there was also the fear that one of us was going to get pinched and sent to jail. I wondered if maybe Sally and I should think about settling down, with both of us earning an honest living. But what could we do? Yes, John had become the manager of the shop, but it had taken him years to get to that position. I didn't want to spend years struggling on nothing in hopes of getting a safe job later. I wanted the good things in life now.

It was when we'd separated again after doing a successful dip, and I was moving on my own through the crowds to our next rendezvous point, that I saw a man checking the contents of his wallet. I didn't notice the size of the wallet, just that he'd pushed it into his pocket, which dangled down away from the rest of his body. It was too good an opportunity to miss. It was a matter of seconds for me to move next to him, hold his coat tail steady with one hand, then slip my fingers into the pocket and take the wallet out without him feeling a thing.

I put the wallet in my inside pocket, then moved swiftly away, easing my way through the crowd, heading for the outside. Once free of the crush of people, I took the wallet out and opened it to check my spoils.

Inside was a wad of banknotes. As I registered their value, I couldn't breathe and I began to shake. I'd never seen so much money in the whole of my life, ever. And never in such large notes! There were two twenty-pound notes, eight ten-pound notes, and three five-pound notes. £135! It was a fortune! I wanted to run straight back home to Seven Dials and find Sally and tell her! We were rich!

But at the same time, I felt scared. Anybody losing this much money would be bound to raise the alarm. I could barely speak when I arrived at the rendezvous point. I could see from the wary expression on Peter's face that he felt the same way.

"We ought to get going," he murmured. "Something this big could lead to a search going on when the man you took it from finds it's gone."

Edward nodded. "You're right," he agreed. "Come on, Dick. Time for all of us to scarper. I suggest we get back north of the river as soon as we can and dispose of this stuff. You and Peter get going, I'll find Sean and Mary and meet up with you afterwards." Then he smiled broadly and clapped me heartily on the back. "Well done, Dick! A haul like that is worth a year of small scores! You must have had sharp eyes to spot the size of that wallet!"

I smiled. I didn't like to tell him it had just been luck.

Chapter Nineteen

Peter and I got back to Seven Dials without a problem. It was as if the large amount of money had given us a new jauntiness in our step that made us travel even faster. Edward, Sean and Mary weren't far behind us, and we met up in Edward's rooms. I wanted to rush off and find Sally and show her the wad of notes, but our rules said it stayed within the gang until the split had been made.

"Let's see it!" said Mary excitedly.

Peter removed the wallet from his jacket, took the large banknotes from it and spread them out on the table.

Sean picked up one of the twenty-pound notes, held it between his fingers, then lifted it to his ear and listened to the paper rustle. His face had a look of sheer delight.

"Rich pickings indeed!" he breathed. He grinned at me. "Well done, Dick! You are a master of your craft!"

"Good old Dick!" grinned Edward. He looked at the notes lying on the table again. "We'd better find a fence who won't cheat us on them."

And so we did. Or, rather, Edward did.

Large-denomination notes like that couldn't be spent.

Or rather, they could, but not by the likes of us, not without some very awkward questions being asked. The only way to get rid of them and turn them into spending money was to sell them to a fence, someone who could pass them on to people rich enough to spend notes that big without questions.

Fences didn't just deal in money; they dealt with all sorts of stolen goods. They bought them cheap from the crooks who got them, then sold them on at a higher price. Just like Larry had done with the handkerchiefs: buying them from the Adelphi gang for ninepence each, and then selling them to shops for a couple of shillings.

Large banknotes were harder to sell because there was a smaller market for them, so fences could bargain hard. But Edward knew a fence he said would give us a fair price.

Sally could hardly believe it when I told her the amount of money I'd taken.

"We've never had such a sum of money before!" she cried. "We have to celebrate!"

"Not until Edward gets the cash from the fence," I cautioned.

In the end, Edward got £4.10s each for the five-pound notes, £8.10s for each of the ten-pound notes, and £18 each for the two twenty-pound notes: a total of £117.10s. As soon as the cash was in my hand, Sally and I went out to the theatre to see an amusing show, and then afterwards to the Coal Hole for drinks. We spent as if money was going out of fashion, but we didn't care. We had money, we were young and happy.

It was soon after this that the shaking and trembling in my hands came back. Luckily, because of the big score I'd made at the Chartists' rally, we had no need to go out and earn more money, otherwise my shaking hands would have got me caught for sure. I told Sally that – because of the money we had – she needn't keep going out and working the omnibuses so often, but she said she needed to keep her hand in, otherwise she'd get rusty and lose her skill. "Use it or lose it, Dick," she said to me. "People like us have to keep in practice, or we're asking for trouble."

"But we're asking for trouble every time we go out," I pointed out to her. "The more times we do the business, the more chances there are of us getting caught. And I like us being together. I don't want to be in prison when you're here at home, or you in prison without me."

"That's what I want as well, Dick," she said. "But living a good life costs money. And you've said it yourself, there ain't no way people like us can earn this kind of money honestly. That's only for the rich and the privileged. The lords and ladies and la-di-dah types. People like us have to work. And I couldn't work cleaning up after someone, seven days a week, fourteen hours a day, for a few shillings a week. Not after the life we've had."

I had to admit, there was no arguing with her on that point. Everything she said was how I felt. Life was unfair. The rich had money and everything they wanted. The poor had nothing and were treated like dirt. The rich wouldn't give you any of their money. Or, if they did, it was charity, and they let you know it, and you had to be beholden and grateful to them and bow down and scrape to them for just the few scraps they gave you. No, life was hard and cruel and unfair. If you wanted better for yourself, you had to take it. No one was going to give it to you.

Then I had another problem to worry about beside my trembling hands. Lately I'd begun to get pains in my legs, crippling pains that sometimes made it difficult for me even to walk. I went to the doctor, and he told me I had rheumatism.

"But only old men get rheumatism!" I protested. "I'm not yet twenty!"

"It's not just age," the doctor told me. "It's damp as well. It gets into the body and into the joints."

"What's the cure for it?" I asked.

"Rest," he said. "You could try an ointment made of ginger root. Some of my patients speak well of it."

I bought a pot of ginger ointment off him and rubbed it into my legs there and then, and took the rest of the pot home with me. When I got back to our rooms, Sally wrinkled her nose, sniffed, and asked, "What's that smell?"

I explained about the ginger ointment, and how I had rheumatism, and the doctor had told me to rest.

"But there's fat chance of that," I said. "I can't earn a living sitting here in our rooms, or lying in bed."

"You don't have to," said Sally. "We've still got some of the money left from that big score you made. And I'll keep working the omnibuses."

"No," I said. "I'm sure I'll be fine in a few days."

But the next day, in spite of the ointment, my legs were worse and by the end of the week the pain in them was so bad I couldn't even walk across our room.

"Right, that's our answer," stated Sally firmly. "You're in no fit state to even go out, let alone work. And we're going to need that money you lifted to pay for the doctor."

And so she went out and carried on working the omnibuses, lifting wallets and purses where she could.

The doctor's bills took a big share of the money we'd put by. Not just the ointment, which I was buying and using by the pot, but different sorts of patent medicines. Some of them were sheer quackery, like putting sheep's wool beneath my bed linen at night, but others were different pills and potions, all of which cost money, and soon our savings were nearly gone.

Sally worked hard, going out nearly every day to lift purses and wallets. On the days when she wasn't out at work she cared for me in our rooms and took me out in the streets, supporting me as we walked. For a while I needed a crutch, which made me feel like an old man. But gradually I began to recover the strength in my legs.

I hadn't been able to work for a long time. Occasionally I saw Peter and Edward in the street when I went walking with Sally and we passed the time of day. They asked after my health, and I asked them how business was going. Although we were polite and friendly to one another when we met, it was obvious from their manner that I was no longer considered part of their gang.

Thanks to Sally's tender care, by the winter of 1850, I was almost back to full health. But then Sally's luck ran out. Just before Christmas she was caught and sentenced to nine months in Westminster Bridewell.

I found myself another couple of stalls and offered to work with them.

At first they were wary, having heard about my problem with my legs. But I was able to persuade them by going to a lady in the street and removing her purse from her skirt pocket while they watched from the other side of the road. It was a risk, but one I had to take. I had to go back to work to raise the money to pay the rent on our rooms, and I wanted to bring Sally treats in prison when I visited her, the way she had for me.

Chapter Twenty

In May 1851, the Great Exhibition opened at Crystal Palace. The Crystal Palace was well named. It was indeed a massive palace, made almost entirely of glass, and inside was all manner of wonders on display. Not just statues and scientific instruments, but huge machines that showed the greatness of Britain's manufacturing industries and engineers, and those from the rest of the Empire. Exhibits were on display from as far away as America, Australia, New Zealand and India, as well as other countries in Europe such as France, Denmark and Switzerland. They included the Koh-i-noor diamond – the largest diamond in the world – a single cast-iron-frame piano from Denmark, the first of its kind ever made in Europe, and a barometer, which used leeches, called the Tempest Prognosticator. There was a display of ancient jewellery from Ireland, from Celtic times, long before the birth of Jesus, which I knew Sally would love to see, and I vowed to show her this and the other wonders when she came out of prison.

As well as all the ancient displays from history, there were new inventions, including a voting machine which counted votes automatically and used a strange system to stop people voting more than once, which I did not quite understand. There was also a public convenience, the first of its kind, for people to go to the toilet, and for which there was a charge of one penny.

The whole place was a marvel of inventions and wonders, and it drew the crowds in their thousands. And with that many people crammed into one place, just as with the Chartists' rally, it offered the prospect of fine pickings for pickpockets and thieves. Me and the two stalls I was ganged up with worked the Great Exhibition for three months, from the time it opened in May until late July. We didn't go there too often, because we would be sure to be spotted as being there too regularly. We went once every two weeks or so, and we generally took fine pickings. On a couple of occasions I went alone and managed to take a few watches and breast-pins from gentlemen, but I only went there if my stalls and I hadn't been at the Exhibition for a few days.

In August, Sally came out of prison. I met her at the prison gates, and saw that she was looking very shaken by her experience inside, although she did her best to insist that it had been "fine and easy".

Sally's experiences in prison had made her cautious, and though she went out on the omnibuses and continued her old trade, she was coming back with fewer and fewer purses and wallets. I knew her nerve was failing her at the last minute, same as it had been with me. But we had to get more money to live on than the both of us were bringing in. And that's how I got in with Bill and Jason.

Bill and Jason were burglars. But they didn't burgle houses.

"We burgle firms and shops," Bill told me. "Much safer, because we do it when there's no one on the premises."

"You burgle a house, you never know when you're going to bump into someone," nodded Jason in agreement. "You might think you'd be safe creeping in during the day, when people are out at work, but sometimes one of them has stayed at home because they're sick…"

"Or because they're on night shift," said Bill.

"Also, there are better pickings at a shop or a factory or an office," said Jason. "You may not get jewellery…"

"But jewellery can be traced," said Bill.

To be honest, I was foolish. I should have asked around about Bill and Jason, found out just how many robberies they'd carried out, and how successful they were. If I'd asked, I would have discovered that they'd only done one before, and they'd nearly got caught, and they'd come away almost empty-handed. But to hear the pair talk, you'd have thought they were the world's most experienced burglars.

It was just three days after I'd first met up with Bill and Jason that they told me about the burglary they'd got planned. It was an office in the City of London. Bill assured me that it would be deserted because the owner was in court that day.

"There's a safe in the office," said Bill. "But it's not a very strong one."

"I can smash it open," Jason told me with a confident grin. "One good smack with a hammer and chisel on the lock and everything in it's ours."

"Your job is to get in through the window and open the door to us," said Bill.

"There's a side window in the back alley round the back of the office," explained Jason. "Only it's very small. Too small for me or Bill to get in."

"But you're just the right size," nodded Jason.

"We smash the window, put you in…"

"And then you open the door and let us in," beamed Jason.

"We come in with the tools, open the safe, and away we go!" smiled Bill.

I thought it over, seeing things that might go wrong. After my experiences of prison, I didn't want to go back in ever again.

"Are you sure the owner's going to be in court?" I asked.

"Absolutely!" nodded Bill. "Me and Jason have cased the joint, and we heard him telling this bloke in a coffee house next door about the subpoena he had, and which day he had to go to court, and complaining how going to court was going to cost him money."

"See?" smirked Jason. "No problems!"

Next day, the three of us set off for the City of London. Jason was carrying a bag with tools, and Bill had a bag to stow the swag once he'd taken it out of the safe. The side window was exactly as they'd described it. It was up an alley, and it was very narrow. Luckily, I was still small for my age, and also thin.

I thought that Bill or Jason would do something clever when breaking the window. I'd heard that burglars put tar or pitch against the glass and then stuck a piece of old sack to it, so that when they broke the glass it didn't smash or fall everywhere and make a noise. Not so with Bill and Jason. Jason took out a hammer and just smashed one of the panes of the glass.

I was startled and looked along the alley, sure that the noise would bring people running to find out what had happened. Bill and Jason didn't seem at all worried. Bill stuck his hand through the hole in the window, slipped the catch, and then pulled the window wide open.

"There!" he said. "Right, quick as you can!"

Jason gave me a leg up and I clambered in over the window-sill, careful not to cut myself on the pieces of broken glass. Once I was in, Bill winked at me.

"We'll be round the front, waiting for you!"

Then they disappeared from sight.

I found myself in a short, narrow, musty corridor. Even though it was daylight, it wasn't easy to see. There were three doors on each side of the corridor, all of them closed.

I made my way along the corridor until I reached the front door. I opened it, and Bill and Jason hurried in, their expressions full of delight and expectation.

"Easy!" crowed Jason.

They hurried to the nearest door. Jason tried the handle. It wasn't locked. "The idiot forgot to lock it!" he chuckled. "One less piece of business for us to do!"

He stepped in through the door, and as he did so I saw a leaded stick swing down and hit him on the head.

Bill stopped, shocked. And then the stick swung upwards and hit him, and he stumbled and fell. I didn't wait. I was already running for the street. Behind me there was a shout of "Stop thief!" accompanied by heavy footsteps.

I got to the door and tried to open it, but I fumbled it, I was so terrified.

Wham! The leaded end of the stick came down on my shoulder, numbing my arm and sending a shock wave of pain through me. I yelled out and fell to the floor, and immediately threw up my hands in surrender. "No more!" I cried out.

The man who'd hit me stood glaring down at me. He was short and stocky and wearing a suit. His hair was parted in the middle and greased down on either side, and he wore a big dark moustache. His expression was the angriest I'd ever seen. His face was so red with anger that I thought he was going to burst a blood vessel. Flecks of spittle were on his lips, and he swung the leaded stick in his hand, as if deliberating whether to hit me anyway.

"Please!" I pleaded with him. "Don't hit me again!"

Chapter Twenty-one

It turned out that the man's court appearance had been cancelled. When he'd heard the glass of the small window smash he'd taken the stick he kept for self-defence and hidden behind his door. He tied up Bill and Jason, who were both still out cold, and then he tied me up. By this time the alarm had been raised and the police turned up and took us to Newgate Prison, where we were charged.

This time, because the charge was burglary, instead of being put up before magistrates, we were sent for trial before a jury. We had no proper defence, and no money to hire a lawyer, so we were found guilty. Bill and Jason were sentenced to seven years each in prison. As the judge turned to me, my legs were like jelly. Seven years in jail! I would die!

"Dick Maybury," intoned the judge. "You are guilty of taking part in this foul crime, but I understand you are eighteen years of age, and therefore – I suspect – a junior partner who came under the influence of these two evil men. I also believe that this is your first offence."

I stared at him, stunned. My first offence? Hardly! I'd

already done time in prison. Then it struck me that those offences were for picking pockets, and in different parts of London. Quickly, I nodded.

"Yes, my lord," I said, gulping, and looking as sorry as I could.

"You will go to prison for eighteen months."

As we were led from the court, a wave of relief washed over me. Bill and Jason had been sentenced to seven years each, but I had got away with eighteen months!

Then, as I was led along the stone-flagged corridor towards the cells, the reality hit me. I was going to be spending eighteen months in jail.

The next miserable eighteen months were like eighteen years to me. I had heard others speak of Newgate Prison as a place where old friends could mingle in the yard. That may have been the case in days gone by but now there was a new regime in place. Newgate had become part of the Silent System, and I was kept in solitary confinement, not allowed to talk to anyone else, not even the warders. What was worse, I was banned from having visitors, so Sally wasn't allowed to come and see me. Nor was I allowed to receive letters or write any myself, so all the time I was in prison I had no news of her, whether she was alive or dead, or if she herself had been arrested and put into prison.

There were some visitors to Newgate, but only those

who'd managed to get a permit from the Lord Mayor of London or a sheriff, and Sally wasn't the class of person who could manage to meet those sort of people.

Newgate was a frightening place. It was where public executions took place in London, on a gallows just outside the prison walls in Newgate Street. Every time there was a hanging, you could tell from the noise outside in the street that carried into the prison. Crowds would gather in their thousands, just to see the poor wretch have his neck stretched. Whole families would turn out for the entertainment, children and babies as well.

Even without the executions, the prison was horrible. Day after day my misery was the same: the same four dank stone walls of my cell with dust-filled light filtering in through the small barred window set high up, too high for me to look out of. I was alone all the time with my thoughts, and the misery of what might be happening to Sally.

I knew that if we stayed in London and kept to this life of crime, all there would be for us would be more and more prison. I had been lucky this time: sentenced to just eighteen months. Next time I would not be so lucky. It was unendurable to think of the rest of my life being spent in a cell such as this, with no one to talk to ever again. Never to see and hold Sally again. Nothing to do but grow old and decay, my body falling prey to old age and pain and illness, until I died. The rest of my life stretching out in monotonous misery was suddenly unbearable. I remembered John and his fiancée, Peg, when I'd met them on Kennington Common, and how happy and settled they seemed. I decided that when I was released, I would return home to Shropshire and see if I could arrange some sort of life for me and Sally, away from the town, in a place where we could start a new beginning together, whatever Sally's reservations might be.

I knew that my father would rage at me, but I hoped to find forgiveness in his heart for me. The Bible talks about forgiveness and atonement, although I knew that was not the aspect of the Bible that my father took. His God was a god of vengeance, of retribution. But still, I was older now. If he saw that I was chastened, and determined to live a good and proper life, perhaps he would forgive me my running away all those years ago. And, even if he didn't, I hoped he would allow me at least to stay in the family home for a while, enough for me to recover and set my feet on the right road.

Chapter Twenty-two

It was early in the morning when I was released from Newgate Prison. I went straight to our rooms in Seven Dials, and there I found Sally getting ready to go out to work. When she saw me she threw her arms around me and cried.

"We have to change our life, or it will be the death of us both," I told her. I then told her about my plan for us to move to Shropshire and start a whole new life.

She looked at me, troubled.

"But I don't know any other life than here in London," she said. "What would I do there?"

"We will find a way," I assured her. "The first thing I must do is go there and make peace with my family, and see if I can come to some kind of arrangement with them for a place to live. My brothers and sister inherited houses from my grandfather. Perhaps we could rent one and find work on the land."

Sally shook her head. "I've never done this sort of thing," she said. "And neither have you, Dick. We are thieves. That's what we do. That's all we know."

"And being thieves may separate us for ever if one of us is transported," I said.

At this she fell silent. Then she nodded. "Go to Shropshire," she said. "And see what you can find for us. Send for me when you are ready."

I kissed her and gave her what little money I had to tide her over while I was away, all except for my stagecoach fare back to Shrewsbury. Then I made my way to Trafalgar Square to catch the coach.

In the time since I had arrived in London, the giant column in the centre of the Square, with the statue of Admiral Lord Nelson at its top, had been completed. Building work in the square was still continuing around the base of Nelson's Column. It was said that more statues were being built, rumours of past kings of England, though some said they would be lions.

I joined the crowds waiting for the coaches, watching out for the one that would take me westward. As I stood by the Square and looked up at the statue of Nelson on his giant column, I reflected that I had first seen this Square as a boy, before Nelson's statue was built. Now, I was leaving it as almost a man. Certainly, with a man's experiences.

The coach that would take me home arrived. I paid my fare, clambered aboard and settled down to the long journey.

The journey back to Shropshire was long. I'd forgotten just how long. Or, perhaps, as I had just been a small boy when I'd first made the journey, my head had been too full of excitement and anticipation of what London held for me, so that I didn't notice the time it took.

As I neared my home village it seemed to me that nothing much had changed. The buildings looked the same as they had when I left, only now they seemed slightly smaller to me. The nearer I came to home, the more my heart fluttered with nerves. What would the reaction be to my return? Would my father be so angry that he'd throw me back out into the street? What would my mother say on seeing me again? Would she be shocked? Happy? Upset? And what of my sister and my brothers?

Finally the coach pulled to a halt in Shrewsbury and I stepped down, my body weary and stiff from the long journey. I walked the five miles to my home village, and finally came back to the place I'd run away from all those years ago. No one seemed to recognize me as I walked down the lane towards the parsonage.

As I neared the heavy dark-brown front door of the parsonage, the fear of what I was about to face built up in me even more, so much so that I nearly turned on my heels and walked away again, unable to face my family. But then I thought: I have faced worse than this. Even if my father rages at me, I will have suffered far worse punishments in the prisons of London and survived. So I gritted my teeth and knocked at the door.

The young servant girl who opened the door was a stranger to me. I asked if Parson Kenton was at home. Her words hit me like a hammer.

"I'm afraid Mr Kenton is dead, sir. The parson now is Parson Whitrigg."

I stared at her, stunned. My father was dead!

"Parson Whitrigg is out at the moment. Would you like to leave a message?"

I stood there, dumb for a brief moment. Then I asked, "What of Parson Kenton's family? His wife and children? Are they still here?"

The girl shook her head.

"No, sir. They have moved to a house a few lanes down."

So the rest of my family were still here! I felt a sense of relief surge through me as I heard those words. My father was dead, but my mother was still alive, and still living in the village.

I got directions from the girl, and then hurried away from the parsonage into the village, and found the lane that my mother had moved to. It was a smaller house with a welcoming wooden fence around it, with a rickety-looking gate, less forbidding than the brick walls and imposing front of the parsonage.

I pushed open the gate, and there, bent over in the front garden picking flowers, I saw my mother. I stopped still, my heart in my mouth. The creaking of the gate made her turn, and she looked at me, puzzled, wondering who this stranger might be. And then she let out a gasp and dropped the flowers, her hand flying to her mouth.

"Dick!"

I ran to her and put my arms around her and hugged her close, and she hugged me back.

"Oh, Dick!" she said. "I thought I'd never see you again!"

I had come home.

Chapter Twenty-three

The reaction from my sister and my younger brother when they saw me wasn't as welcoming as that of my mother, but then things had been difficult between us before I went away. They were polite, but that was all. I thought they seemed suspicious of me. The problem was that I didn't want to tell them too much about my life in London in case I gave away the fact that I'd been a criminal ever since I left home, because I was sure that if they discovered that, they'd urge my mother to turn me out of the house. So, instead, all conversations between me and my two siblings were polite, but not warm. And my mother, although initially so pleased to see me, soon began to worry again about the everyday things of life. Especially money, of which it appeared there was very little.

I found out that my father had died not long before of yellow jaundice, which he had been suffering from for the last five years. On his death my mother had to vacate the parsonage for the new preacher, and was now living in this cottage, on a weekly sum paid to her by the Wesleyan fund for the benefit of the widows of ministers. This was the pension on which she lived.

My elder brother had married and was now living and working in Manchester. My younger brother and my sister were both still at home, though my sister was engaged to be married and would soon be leaving to make her own life with her new husband.

I discovered the houses that had been left to them had been sold some years before. I therefore knew that the hope of myself and Sally finding ourselves a home in one of my late grandfather's properties was a dead end.

I stayed with my family at the cottage for seven weeks, and during that time I explored the possibilities of work for Sally and me, but it soon became obvious there was very little chance of it. Certainly not the kind of work that either Sally or I could easily fit into, and would earn us sufficient to have a life with some small luxuries that we'd grown accustomed to. So, at the end of those seven weeks I said goodbye to my mother and my brother and sister and, promising to write and keep them informed of my doings, I returned to London, and to Sally. In my heart, I felt they were glad to see me go.

I found Sally to be very low in spirits when I returned. She had been working the omnibuses as before, but had had a couple of narrow scrapes and nearly got caught. In one of them she only managed to avoid arrest by leaping from the bus and running away, losing a shoe in the process. She had managed to lose herself in the crowd in Covent Garden before making her way back to our rooms.

She was very keen to find out how it had gone in Shropshire, and if I'd been able to find a house for us.

"All the houses my family owned have been sold," I told her. "My mother struggles to live on her small pension she gets from the church, so I don't think there is any chance for us."

Sally's face fell. "Perhaps we could find work there and rent a house?" she asked hopefully.

I shook my head. "There is very little work there, except farm labouring, or working as servants. I don't think that would suit either of us."

Sally fell silent for a moment. Then finally she asked: "So, what are we to do?"

"I thought I might try street selling," I said. "It's clean and honest work, and if I sell enough we should be able to live in some comfort."

"What would you sell?" she asked.

At this question, I fell silent. I had to admit, I did not know. "I'll think of something," I said. And I looked at her with a fierce determination. "Give me just one day and I will find a way to make our fortune in an honest way," I promised her.

Sally nodded and patted my hand with a smile. "In the meantime, we need to eat," she said. "I will do one last trip and earn us our dinner. And, who knows, I may land us enough to get a whole new start!"

Later that day I stood waiting for Sally at one end of the Strand, expecting her to step down from the omnibus and come towards me, smiling, with a pocketbook or a purse hidden about her. Instead, I saw an omnibus pull to a halt, heard a shouting and commotion on it, saw a police constable running along the Strand towards it. Then I saw Sally being dragged off the bus, the constable holding her by one arm and a very angry man holding her tightly by the other. Sally was crying and protesting her innocence, but the expression on the face of the man showed that he wasn't moved by her appeals, and the constable's face had the satisfied look of a man who has just moved one step nearer to promotion. As I watched Sally being dragged away I knew it was all over for her. And for us.

Epilogue

Sally was tried, found guilty and sentenced to be transported. I sat in the court watching. When she discovered her fate she almost collapsed in the dock.

I tried to see her afterwards, but she was whisked away to prison, and shortly after sent to a different jail outside London on the coast. That was her last stop before she set sail for Australia.

I don't think I had ever felt so miserable and lonely in my life. Once, in my madness, I thought about committing a crime so that I could be transported with her. But I'm told that Australia is a large place, and convicts are sent all over it.

My heart was heavy, but I was determined to continue with the original plan – to live without crime.

I found work as a patterer. A patterer is someone who earns their living by calling out the news in the streets to sell the latest broadsheets, or shouting out to advertise the wares of others. It would never give me as much money as I earned from picking pockets, but it was honest employment.

Last night I dreamt that Sally was still with me, and that she'd found work on a market stall selling fruit and vegetables. Her outgoing personality was just the sort to attract customers as she shouted the latest bargain prices for the goods on the stall. But when I woke up, I was alone, as always, and Sally was half way around the world, and gone from my life for ever.

Author's Note

This story is based on interviews given by a man calling himself Dick, to the Victorian sociologists Henry Mayhew and John Binny, as part of their study into the London criminal underworld. Dick was interviewed in 1861, when he was 31, by John Binny for the fourth volume of Mayhew's work *London Labour and the London Poor*.

At that time he was interviewed, Dick was described as a shabby middle-sized bearded man. He was living in a lodging house in a poor area of London with his girlfriend and he earned his living by selling broadsheets in the streets of London.

After this interview in 1861 Dick faded from history. There is no further mention of him in any criminal records after that time.

Historical Note

Crime and punishment in Victorian England

At the start of the nineteenth century there were over 200 capital crimes (crimes for which hanging was the punishment). In 1823 Sir Robert Peel's government reduced the number of capital offences by over a hundred, and from 1832 brought in various Parliamentary Bills to reduce the number even further. In 1832 shoplifting, and stealing horses, cattle and sheep were removed; sacrilege and letter stealing were taken off the list in 1834, and unauthorized return from transportation in 1835. Forgery and coining followed in 1836, with arson, burglary and theft from a dwelling house in 1837. By 1862 there were only four offences for which a convicted person could be hanged: murder, high treason, arson in a royal dockyard and piracy.

Child criminals in Victorian times

In the early nineteenth century no distinction was made between child criminals and adult criminals. They were all put into a common jail regardless of age, and punished with equal severity. Until 1808 picking pockets was punishable by death. In 1814 five child criminals under the age of fourteen years old were hanged for stealing, the youngest being just eight years old.

One boy, by the age of ten, had spent much of his young life in jail for various offences, such as: possession of seven scarves for which he received two months in jail; possession of half a sovereign: one month in jail; being a rogue and a vagabond: two months in jail; larceny (theft): one month in jail and whipping. There are records of children aged as young as eight being sent to jail for stealing "a penny tart".

As the nineteenth century progressed, various reformers took up the causes of children, most of them realizing that the majority of crimes that children committed were the result of extreme poverty. Many of these social reformers were Quakers, such as Elizabeth Fry and Samuel Hoare. As a result of the pressure they, and others, put on Parliament, a series of Acts were passed to improve the lot of children, especially with regard to those arrested for petty crimes.

The Juvenile Offenders Act of 1847 allowed children under the age of fourteen to be tried before two magistrates, rather than in the higher courts. Between 1854 and 1858 other Acts were passed that replaced prison with juvenile institutions for minor offences.

Along with these reforms, other campaigners took action at street level. In 1870 Dr Thomas Barnardo opened his first orphanage in Stepney Causeway.

The great novelist, Charles Dickens, strongly influenced the call for reform and a more sympathetic view of child criminals in Victorian times through novels such as *Oliver Twist*.

Places Mentioned in the Story

Bow Street Magistrates' Court

Bow Street Magistrates' Court was the most famous magistrates' court in England. The first court was established there in 1740. In 1749, Henry Fielding set up London's first professional police service, known as The Bow Street Runners. In 1805 the Bow Street Horse Patrol was set up, the first uniformed police unit in Britain.

Famous defendants who appeared at Bow Street Magistrates' Court have included Oscar Wilde, Dr Crippen, Ronnie and Reggie Kray, and Emmeline and Christabel Pankhurst.

Bow Street Magistrates' Court closed in July 2006, to be converted into a hotel.

Flower and Dean Street

Flower and Dean Street was a road at the centre of the notorious Spitalfields rookery in London's Whitechapel. In 1883 it was described as "perhaps the foulest and most dangerous street in the whole metropolis." Honest but poor people were forced to live there alongside villains and crooks because lodgings there were amongst the cheapest in London.

Newgate Prison

Newgate Prison was originally built in 1188 at the site of a gate in the Roman London Wall. Over centuries it was enlarged, but was destroyed in the Great Fire of London in 1666. It was again rebuilt in 1672. In 1780 the prison was attacked by mobs during the Gordon Riots and set on fire. The prison was rebuilt again in 1782 and divided into two areas: a Common area for poor prisoners, and a State area for those who were able to afford comfortable accommodation. In 1783 the gallows used for public executions was moved from Tyburn to the outside of Newgate Prison in Newgate Street. Public executions stopped in 1868, and after that date executions were carried out on a gallows inside the prison. The prison closed in 1902 and was demolished in 1904. The Central Criminal Court (known as the Old Bailey) now stands on the site.

Famous prisoners jailed in Newgate included Daniel

Defoe (author of *Robinson Crusoe*), Ben Jonson (playwright and poet – jailed for killing another actor in a duel), Captain Kidd, the pirate, and Jack Sheppard, the notorious highwayman.

Seven Dials

This area of London by Covent Garden was a notorious slum in mid-Victorian times. It had originally been developed by Thomas Neale in the early 1690s as a place for the well-to-do to live. Where seven roads met a tall column was erected, each side of the column having a sundial facing a different road. The original sundial column was taken down in 1773, as the area deteriorated and the authorities feared the sundial might be damaged.

Trafalgar Square.

Trafalgar Square commemorates the victory by Admiral Lord Nelson's fleet over the French, and Nelson's death, at the Battle of Trafalgar in 1805 during the Napoleonic Wars. The first stage of the Square was completed in 1840. Nelson's Column was constructed between 1843 and 1845. In 1845 fountains were built to break up the large space so that it would not be easy for "riotous assemblies" to be held there. The four lions at the base of the Column were added in 1867.

Glossary

dipper = pickpocket

fan = feel someone's clothing for a purse or money before picking their pocket

maltooler = pickpocket who steals from people on buses

mark = victim

patterer = someone who earns their living by calling out the news in the streets to sell the latest broadsheets, or shouting out to advertise wares

peach = to give information to the police (modern slang: grass)

quack = unlicensed doctor, with no real medical expertise

rookery = slum area

stall = thief's accomplice whose job is to get in the way of any pursuer

stickman = pickpocket or shoplifter's accomplice who gets passed the stolen goods

tooler = pickpocket

vagrant = a homeless person

wipe = handkerchief